Schubert

Communications Cables
and Transmission Systems

Communications Cables and Transmission Systems

by Werner Schubert

SIEMENS AKTIENGESELLSCHAFT

CIP-Kurztitelaufnahme der Deutschen Bibliothek

Schubert , Werner
Communications cables and transmission systems. – 1. Aufl. –
Berlin, Munich [München] : Siemens-Aktiengesellschaft, [Abt. Verl.], 1975.
   Dt. Ausg. u. d. T.: Schubert , Werner : Nachrichtenkabel
   und Übertragungssysteme.
   ISBN 3-8009-1218-X

Title of German original edition:
Nachrichtenkabel und Übertragungssysteme

ISBN 3-8009-1218-X

Published by Siemens Aktiengesellschaft, Berlin and Munich
© 1976 by Siemens Aktiengesellschaft, Berlin and Munich

Printed in Western Germany

Preface

More than a hundred and twenty years ago the first overhead telephone line to be used in Germany was installed between Berlin and Frankfurt am Main. As a result of a Government Act in 1848 for the election of a national assembly, in the church of St. Paul in Frankfurt, it was put into operation and was, at first, only used by Government officials.

This project involved one of the earliest functions of electrical engineering; namely, that of electrically transmitting informations over long distances. Even at that time electrical enginnering was beginning to be divided into the branches of heavy and light current engineering, and is still so divided today – despite the not inconsiderable overlapping that is still existing partly between these two spheres.

In the course of the last few decades one of the most important ideas that has been developed in the light current engineering industry is the concept of communications engineering, which includes the complete electrical transmission of information. Every electrical communications system consists, principally, of three main parts; the transmitter, the transmission route, and the receiver. Whilst the fundamental purpose of the transmitter is to convert acoustic or optical signals into electrical signals, and the fundamental purpose of the receiver is to make the corresponding conversion back to acoustic or optical signals, the transmission route represents a purely electrical system. If we omit the subject of radiation in space, then the wire line is always an essential part of the transmission route.

Initially, the transmission of information via wires was confined to open wire lines which, unfortunately, were frequently the cause of interruptions as a result of climatic influences. Open wire lines, today, have practically ceased to be of importance in all countries, in particular for so called long-distance traffic, because the introduction of valve repeaters and, more recently, the introduction of transistor repeaters has made it possible to cover any distance with communications cables.

When telecommunications engineering started, copper wires embedded in the natural substance called gutta-percha were used for communications cables. In addition to paper, plastics (with excellent electrical properties) have been increasingly adopted as insulating materials and are now gaining equal importance as cable sheathing.

The purpose of this book is to give those who are interested in the engineering of communications cables a general idea of both the theories of transmission engineering and the technological problems involved. Some of the techniques bordering on this subject are also discussed.

To give a clear but simple picture, and to ensure the book can be used as a convenient reference work for practical engineers, detailed descriptions of manufacturing processes and the derivations of equations have been omitted.

To complete the subject, some brief references may be made here to the basic requirements in the design and planning of communication cable systems. For this purpose it is of vital importance to know the number and type of the various connections to the respective terminal points. It is then necessary to assume a thorough knowledge of the planned cable route, not only as regards its course, but also with reference to the conditions of the ground in which it will be laid, the aggressive properties of the soil and possible external interference with the communications cable from, for example, high-tension lines, lightning etc.

On the basis of such data, and after taking into consideration possible future extensions in the number of connections, the most economic and technically-efficient cable can then be designed. In designing the cable the electrical problems, or rather, perhaps, the problems of transmission engineering, are the most important. The next problem which must always be taken into consideration are the mechanical and chemical stresses to which the cable may later be subjected during the cable-laying process or in its operation.

Special thanks are due here to all those colleagues whose collaboration has contributed to the success of this book, particularly Mr. Klaus Beck of the Export Sales department, Telecommunication Cables Division, who chiefly contributed to the success of this English Edition.

Munich, February 1976

SIEMENS AKTIENGESELLSCHAFT

Contents

1. The components of communications cables

1.1. General introduction

A *communications cable* consists essentially of metal conductors, their insulating coverings, the wrapping for the cable core, the sheathing and the protective coverings.

This Chapter gives a description of the materials used for the conductors, the various insulating materials, and the design of wires, together with a discussion of symmetrical and unsymmetrical components (elements in the stranding).

The arrangements discussed below are representative for the standard types in use today.

The following concepts form an introduction to the subject.

(a) *Conductors*

A conductor is made of metal; its purpose is to convey electrical charge carriers.

(b) *Wires*

A wire is a conductor, covered with insulation.

(c) *Lines*

A line (also termed a loop) contains several – at least two – conductors. According to the definition of the German Association of Electrical Engineers the line in a *star quad*, or in a *DM-quad* is called a *side circuit* or trunk line. The two wires in a pair, or side circuit, are also called, in post office usage, *dual wires*.

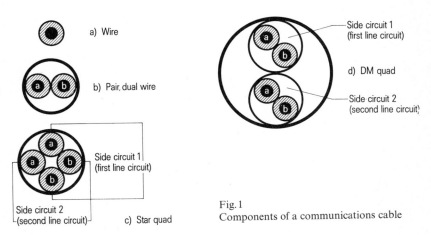

a) Wire

b) Pair, dual wire

Side circuit 1
(first line circuit)

Side circuit 2
(second line circuit)

c) Star quad

Side circuit 1
(first line circuit)

d) DM quad

Side circuit 2
(second line circuit)

Fig. 1
Components of a communications cable

The simplest line is a side circuit. This consists of, in an *open wire line* two conductors, or, in a *cable*, of two wires (a *single pair* when the stranding is made with pairs, or side circuit 1 or side circuit 2 in a quad). A third speech unit, the *phantom line*, can be formed from the two side circuits in a quad. Such cable lines are known as *symmetrical lines*. A *coaxial line*, however, is known as an *unsymmetrical line*.

a) Symmetrical

Inner conductor
Dielectric
Outer conductor

b) Coaxial

Fig. 2   Types of lines

It is generally the number of dual wires which defines a cable. It is thus of no consequence whether the cable consists of pairs, star quads, DM-quads or coaxial pairs. Two dual wires make up a star quad, whilst a coaxial pair is equivalent to a single dual wire.

Thus, a cable containing one coaxial pair and eight star quads accordingly has 17 dual wires, or is a 17-pair cable. The German Federal Postal and Telegraph Authority describes its *telephone cables* as *form cables* (the above example thus being known as form 17 cable). Further letters of the alphabet are used to distinguish different types of cable with the same number of pairs, such as for example, *long-distance CF cable* (TFFk) or *long-distance coaxial cable* (KxFk).

Chapter 2 discusses the various designs of communications cables – the *cable core*, the *cable sheath*, the *protective coverings* and the *armouring*. Some relevant explanations of VDE specification 08 16 (devised by the German Association of Electrical Engineers) are given, together with some interesting facts. The various specifications and standards relevant to materials and electrical properties can be obtained from VDE 08 16.

Some particularly interesting cable designs are also explained and illustrated.

1.1.1. Conductors

The communications cables used in Germany today have conductors made exclusively of electrolytic-copper, with an *electrical conductivity* (at a temperature of 20 °C) of:

$$\varkappa_{20} \geqq 57 \, \frac{S \cdot m}{mm^2}$$

here S is the unit of conductivity in $\frac{1}{\Omega}$ (Siemens).

During the last decade continuous research has been made in an attempt to replace copper by aluminium conductors. Developments abroad are already so far advanced that experimental sections of more importance are now equipped with cables containing aluminium conductors.

12

1.1.2. Insulating materials

The gutta-percha and rubber insulation which was formerly used for outdoor cables is nowadays of no importance. These insulating materials have been replaced by, for example, paper, *polyvinilchloride, styroflex* and *polythene*, materials of high mechanical and electrical quality, with the result that it is possible to make communications cables having smaller-diameter conductors, to reduce the cable diameter and weight and yet improve its transmission characteristics. The insulation materials used for communications cables have a low *relative dielectric constant* ε_r and a low *dissipation factor* tan δ.

With every increase in the frequency range required to transmit a message electrically, the more strict become the conditions demanded of the insulating cover which form the dielectric[1]. The insulating material also prevents the conductors from coming into metallic contact with each other.

The *paper* most frequently used for cables is pure unbleached sulphate pulp paper without any addition of fillers, etc. When dry, cabling paper has good electrical properties, i.e. sufficient dielectric strength, a low dissipation factor (tan $\delta \approx 3 \cdot 10^{-3}$ at a frequency of 800 Hz), and a low relative dielectric constant ε_r (2.1 ... 2.3).

In its natural state, cabling paper has a light-brown/beige colour. All such papers are of course special papers, the properties and tolerances of which are described in the German Industrial Standard (DIN) 46450. All papers used for cabling in Germany must satisfy this standard.

Paper for cabling is produced from wood-pulp fibres without any adhesive addition. In Europe, pine-wood pulp is used almost exclusively. In America, however, and in some other countries, the paper is usually made of cellulose mixtures (e.g., wood, manila, plants of the hemp family, and cotton). The paper is produced by various technical processes. On the *Fourdrinier paper machine* for example, a metal sieve moves, like a conveyor belt, on supporting and guiding rollers. The paper pulp is supplied, at the start of the process, with a 2% content of solid bodies. As the sieve moves forward the water-content is removed by suction and the moisture-free paper is continuously rolled onto drums at the end of the cycle. Due to the direction in which the sieve moves, the fibres in the paper are, mainly, longitudinally aligned. By various shaking movements, transverse to the direction of motion, a greater or lesser transverse orientation of the fibres can be superimposed on their longitudinal direction (the longitudinal-to-transverse ratio is approximately 2 : 1).

In a *cylinder paper machine*, however, a cylindrical sieve has approximately one-third its circumference dipped in the paper-pulp, which has its moisture removed by having the water extracted via the inside of the drum.

---

[1] A material which does not conduct electricity or is a poor conductor of it.

The *insulation resistance* of paper for cables depends on its moisture content. On delivery, this is approximately 8%. The 10,000 M$\Omega \cdot$ km insulation-resistance which usually has to be guaranteed for the wires is associated, however, with a moisture of only 4%. It is, consequently, necessary to dry cable cores having paper insulated wires.

Paper-string is one of the items produced from the strips of paper by special processes. The expression "string" has been adopted from on older technique. In fact, it is a twisted strip of paper and, therefore, really a paper yarn.

Another way of insulating cables with paper has been developed in America, whereby the conductor is insulated in paper-pulp in an extrusion process. This type of insulation, which has been introduced into America and Japan by a few firms, is known as a *"pulped wire"*.

Within the last few decades an immense variety of plastics materials has been making ever deeper inroads into the spheres of consumer-economics and applied technology. The original idea of a plastics material is due to the realisation that some purposely-developed plastics have, at least, equally good (and frequently better) characteristics than the materials previously used (for example their mechanical and electrical properties, their ability to withstand stresses and their suitability for machining).

The development of plastics has simultaneously led to new technological processes, with the result that the end product is sometimes considerably less expensive.

Many new concepts and terms have been introduced by the chemistry of plastics. The essential ideas in this sphere will be explained in the following text.

Monomers: tiny molecules in raw chemical products of homogeneous or non-uniform types.

Polymerization: by polymerization, several monomers (also several hundreds or even thousands of monomers) are formed into macro-molecules. Depending on the method of syntheses, there are various types of macro-molecules.

Linear macro-molecules: or chain molecules: these have only two bonds, one on each side.

—○—○—○—○—○—○—○—○—○—○—○—○—○—

Fig. 3   Linear macro-molecules

Branched macro-molecules: these have bonds on more than two sides.

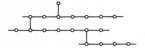

Fig. 4   Branched macro-molecules

Cross-linked macro-molecules: these, for the most part, have bonds at three points which gives the macro-molecule its more spherical shape.

Fig. 5   Cross-linked macro-molecules

Co-polymerization: implies the combination of polymerized plastics to change their initial properties, i.e., various monomer plastics are polymerized together.

Thermosetting plastics (Duromers): plastics which, after being processed, form hardened-and-set products without any cutting. Any heat subsequently applied will scarcely change their state once it has become set. Such plastics are, for example, epoxy resins and polyurethanes.

Elastomers: substances which have elastic properties similar to rubber depending on temperature.

Thermoplastics (plastomers): plastics which can be repeatedly reshaped by the subsequent application of heat, without their molecules losing their macro-structure. Excessive heat, unfortunately, changes the plastic. All the polymers (e.g., polyvinylchloride (PVC), polythene (PE) and polystyrene) belong to this group. The properties of PE and PVC are given in VDE 0209. Thermoplastics have a much higher coefficient of expansion than metals, and can be partially (or completely) dissolved by the application of chemical solvents.

When affected by aromatic hydrocarbons and chloro-hydrocarbons, polythene swells. The smaller the density of the polythene, the greater is the amount of swelling. PE is resistant to water, salt solutions, and to many acids and alkalis of weak or average strength. PE is attacked by powerful oxidising agents such as sulphuric-acid fumes, chromosulphuric acid, chlorosulfonic acid and the halogens (bromine, iodine, and fluorides). This is also true of xylene, benzene, and the aromatic oils. Materials which cause surface effects, such as cleaning materials and detergents (e.g., "Pril" and soap) may cause tension cracks on any PE parts subject to mechanical stress. Thus, when testing PE accessories, in the so-called "soaping process", no such materials may be used. To process the cable sheathing or protective covering, some 2 % of soot/lampblack is added to the natural-coloured PE, which has a translucent milky colour, to make it ultraviolet-resistant. To date, it has not been possible to provide this resistance with any other colouring material.

15

PVC, like PE, is also attacked by acids, alkalis and to some extent by salt solutions and the majority of the solvents. It is possible to make PVC largely resistant to oil by adding special mixtures. Consequently, it is used in this way for the protective covering of pipe-line cables.

1.2. Design of the wires for symmetrical components

1.2.1. Paper-insulated wires

The simplest form of paper insulation involves the spinning of one or more layers of paper strip onto the conductor, with at least a 25% overlap. Depending on the method of spinning, there are produced *hollow* or *tubular wires* with a certain amount of air-space between the conductor and the insulating paper, and *solid wires* with very little intermediate air-space.

It is often desirable to have as little insulating material as possible adjacent to the conductor. To maintain the *resultant dielectric constant* ε at a low value it is possible to spin the paper layer in such a way that there occurs a fold in the middle of the paper strip. It is, however, more satisfactory to apply a paper yarn (string) beneath the paper strip.

The resultant dielectric constants vary between 1.6 and 1.9 depending upon the design, i.e., the amount of air in the insulation covering. Tubular wires are only used for cables intended to cover short distances such as *subscriber cables*, and *inter exchange trunk cables* in local networks overseas.

For communication cable installation where the *mutual capacity* C_B and the *attenuation constant*, α, must be of a low value – as is necessary, for example, with symmetrical main or long-distance cables, and also for subscriber cables which have to cover long distances, the material and design of the cable (when using paper insulation) are so chosen that the resultant dielectric constant is between 1.4 and 1.45 *(string-wound wires)*.

1.2.2. Wires insulated with plastics

PVC-insulated wires

Pure polyvinylchloride (PVC) is a thermoplastic synthetic material based on chlorine, carbon and hydrogen atoms. In its pure form PVC is hard and brittle. By adding so-called *plasticizers* it is possible to alter its tensile strength, its compression strength, its hardness and its softening point. *Fillers* which are *poor electrolytes* such as chalk or kaolin reduce the cost of the insulation material. *Dyes* and *lubricants* are further additives. PVC, in its above form can be considered a mixture which, by further processing, is rolled and prepared as granular material which is then applied to the conductor, by an extrusion process, at about 180 °C.

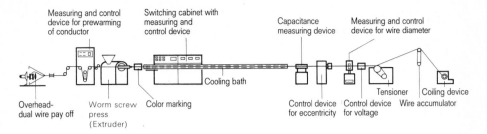

Fig. 6 Different stages in the extrusion of plastics-covered cable

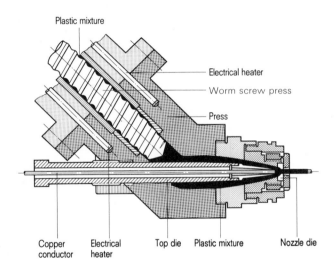

Fig. 7 Simplified sectional drawing of an extruder

The relative dielectric constant of PVC insulating material varies between 3 and 8, depending on the addition of plasticizers, dye-stuffs, fillers, and on the value of the ambient temperature. The dissipation factor tan δ is relatively high; depending on the ambient temperature, it varies between $2 \cdot 10^{-2}$ to approx. $7 \cdot 10^{-2}$ up to a frequency of 1500 Hz.

Generally, therefore, PVC is only used as an insulating material for insulated jumper-wires, installation wires, switchboard cables and istallation cables; consequently, it is used mostly for internal installations.

PE-insulated wires

Polythene (PE) is a thermoplastic synthetic material based on hydrocarbon atoms. PE has exceptional electrical properties. It is, consequently, very extensively used for wire insulation of communication cables in subscriber networks. Conductors insulated with solid or cellular PE, when stranded as star quads, can also be used with a carrier frequency system (Z12; 108 kHz). In the frequency range 50 to 10^6 Hz the dissipation factor tan δ of high-pressure polythene is between 1 and $3 \cdot 10^{-4}$, and the relative dielectric constant ε_r in the same range, is between 2.1 and 2.3.

The current method of insulating conductors is to use solid or cellular PE with insulation thickness between some 0.2 and 0.3 mm. The PE is applied to the conductor in an extruder.

Solid-PE   Cellular-PE

Fig. 8   PE-insulated wires

For solid PE insulation, direct use is made of the granulated PE, supplied by the manufacturers, in the required colours. If a vaporising agent is added to the granulated PE, then, because of the thermal decomposition of the vaporising agent, it starts to foam upon extrusion. The gas thus produced forms tiny, generally closed cavities within the insulation covering so that, in contrast to solid PE insulation, the cellular method of insulating the wires provides a smaller resultant dielectric constant (Where the cell forming process occupies some 40 to 50% of the covering, $\varepsilon \approx 1.6$).

A recent method of insulating conductors with solid PE is suitable for the conductor-enamelling process. In this method several conductors are simultaneously drawn through a thin PE solution (PE dispersion = PED). The dispersion (the PE particles floating in the liquid) adheres to the conductor. By the application of heat, the fluid evaporates and the PE melts together in a solid compact, insulation covering of PE.

Styroflex-insulated wires

Styroflex, which is a trade name for polystyrene, is also a thermoplastic synthetic material based on hydrocarbon atoms. To reduce crack formation and brittleness, polystyrene (with long molecular chains) is used for the manufacture of cables. The elasticity which styroflex requires to have during processing is also achieved by stretching the longitudinally-orientated chains of molecules.

At a frequency of 800 Hz the dissipation factor $\tan \delta$ is between 0.1 to $0.2 \cdot 10^{-3}$, and the relative dielectric constant (ε_r) is approximately 2.4.

Due to these satisfactory properties, i.e., lower leakage losses, styroflex makes a particularly suitable insulation for the wires of long-distance cables. Wires are used with thread and tape of styroflex which are spun onto the conductor by methods basically the same as those described in 1.2.1. In comparison with every other known method of designing wires for symmetrical components, the wires insulated with the normally-used type of styroflex have the lowest value for the resultant dielectric constant in the cable ($\varepsilon \approx 1.15$ to 1.2).

1.3. Symmetrical components

The components so far discussed, are manufactured from wire designs described in greater detail in 1.2. They are also known as *stranding elements*.

A single wire, in contrast to a symmetrical line, is treated as an unsymmetrical component. The single wire is only used for signal and metering purposes in outdoor cables.

In a symmetrical line both conductors, in their operating condition, are at the same potential with respect to the cable sheathing (screen), and with respect to earth. When designing a cable it is therefore possible to assume, with sufficient accuracy that, if the material of the conductors and their nominal diameter is the same, and the design of the wires is the same, then each of the two conductors will have the same ohmic line-resistance, and that the *line inductance* L will be equally distributed along both lines. When the longitudinal resistance refers, as is usual in practice, not to the conductor but to the line the term used is the *loop resistance R* (twice the conductor resistance). In a symmetrical line the properties of both conductors are equal relative to earth, metal sheath or metal screen (wire-to-earth capacity) and they have the same leakage.

1.3.1. A pair

A pair is the simplest symmetrical unit in a strand. In Germany it is relatively seldom used. However, it is used in installation cables and as a screened pair for the radio broadcasting.

High numbers of pairs are used in subscriber cables abroad. The two wires belonging to a line are mutually twisted into a pair. The distance between a selected, fixed, point and the point at which a specified wire again assumes the same position as that at the fixed point, after turning through 360°, is known as the *twist length* (or pitch). To minimise cross-talk between the pairs, special twist lengths are specified.

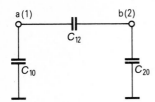

Fig. 9
Equivalent circuit for a line
(pair) with a screen

The symbols in Figure 9 have the following significance:

C_{12} is the capacitance between the two conductors (a and b)

C_{10} and C_{20} are respectively the *capacitances* of conductor "a" and conductor "b" *to earth.*

The *unbalance to ground* (earth coupling) of a pair is $C_{10} - C_{20}$.

The *mutual capacitance*, C_B, of the pair is obtained from the three capacitances C_{12}, C_{10} and C_{20} as

$$C_B = C_{12} + \frac{C_{10} \cdot C_{20}}{C_{10} + C_{20}}.$$

1.3.2. Star quads

The most-frequently used stranding element in Germany is the star-quad. In the subscriber network of the German Federal Post and Telegraph Authority (DBP) (i.e., in *local subscriber connection cables* and in *interexchange trunk cables*) use is made of star quads with *tubular paper wires*, with *paper string wires*, or with *solid PE-insulated wires* where the conductors are 0.4 mm-diameter, or for 0.6 and 0.8 conductor diameter of paper string wires and, recently, of *cellular PE-insulated wires*. In a few instances, star quads, with paper string wires or cellular PE-insulated wires, are used where the conductor diameter is 0.9 mm.

For CF transmission, star quads with paper-string wires or solid or cellular PE-insulation, are also used in the Z 12[1] CF system. The V60[2] system, with an upper transmission frequency of some 252 kHz uses star quads with paper-string-insulated wires. In this system the required cross-talk attenuation is maintained by using two separate cables for the two audio directions, i.e., one main line in each cable for each system.

---

[1] Z12, a two-wire system for twelve audio channels with frequency bands of 0.3 to 3.4 kHz each on one main line. The upper transmission frequency is 108 kHz.

[2] V60, a four-wire system for 60 channels (each channel covers an audio-frequency band of 0.3 to 3.4 kHz).

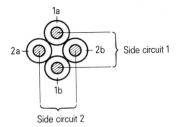

Fig. 10
Schematic drawing of a star quad,
looking at the startend of the cable

In the trunk cable network of the DBP star quads with styroflex string wires are used. Two such cables are used in the V120 four-wire system (120 speech channels, at frequency bands ranging from 0.3 to 3.4 kHz).

The star quad is popular in Germany, because its side circuit lines have a lower mutual-capacity than the twisted pairs in cables.

The line attenuation in the side circuit lines of star quads is also, therefore, lower.

The four wires in a star quad are simultaneously stranded with a twist. As shown in Fig. 10, the two wires in one line are always diametrically opposite one another. Every star quad thus consists of two symmetrical lines, which are also called main lines.

In Germany there are four different types of star quads, which have different applications and different transmission characteristics.

St III A star quad without using any phantom line for subscriber cables (local cables)

St I A star quad which uses no phantom circuit, for long range telephone cables

St A star quad which uses the phantom circuit for cables on special networks

F A star quad which uses the phantom circuit for railway telecommunications cables of the German Federal Railways (DB).

With specified star quads it is thus possible, by connecting phantom transformers to the ends of the line, to produce a third line circuit, the *phantom circuit*, from the two side circuits (Fig. 11). For this purpose, according to VDE 0816, only star quads of St or F quality may be used.

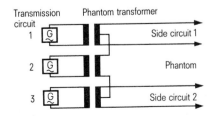

Fig. 11
Phantom circuit made from
two side circuits

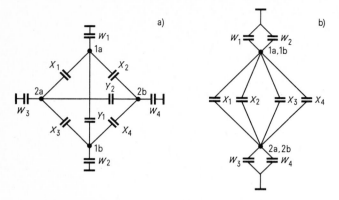

Fig. 12. Partial capacitances of a star quad, on the right, in a phantom circuit

By reason of the parallel connection of the two conductors from side circuits 1 and 2, the loop resistance of the phantom circuit is only half as large as that of the each side circuit.

The mutual capacitance of the side and phantom circuits can be derived from the partial capacities of the star quad as shown in Fig. 12.

If the partial capacitances are known, the mutual capacitance of the side and phantom circuits can be calculated as follows.

$$C_{\text{B side circuit 1}} = y_1 + \frac{x_1 \cdot x_3}{x_1 + x_3} + \frac{x_2 \cdot x_4}{x_2 + x_4} + \frac{w_1 \cdot w_2}{w_1 + w_2}$$

$$C_{\text{B side circuit 2}} = y_2 + \frac{x_1 \cdot x_2}{x_1 + x_2} + \frac{x_3 \cdot x_4}{x_3 + x_4} + \frac{w_3 \cdot w_4}{w_3 + w_4}.$$

In the phantom line, conductors 1a and 1b and also 2a and 2b, are connected via the transformer.

$$C_{\text{B phantom}} = (x_1 + x_2 + x_3 + x_4) + \frac{(w_1 + w_2) \cdot (w_3 + w_4)}{w_1 + w_2 + w_3 + w_4}.$$

In this treatment, if the small differences between the similar partial capacitances are neglected, and the error is trivial, then

$$x_1 = x_2 = x_3 = x_4 = x \,,$$

$$y_1 = y_2 = y \quad \text{and}$$

$$w_1 = w_2 = w_3 = w_4 = w$$

hence,

$$C_{\text{B side circuit 1.2}} = x + y + \frac{w}{2}$$

$$C_{\text{B phantom}} \qquad = 4x + w\,.$$

In a star quad the ratio of the partial capacitances is

$$x : y : w = 5 : 1 : 10\,.$$

Hence, from the above simplified equations, one can deduce the well known ratio

$$\frac{C_{\text{B phantom}}}{C_{\text{B side circuit}}} \approx 2.7\,.$$

Although in pairs, because of faults in symmetry between the two wires, there is only one earth-coupling e (see 1.3.1.), in a star quad there are six *inherent quad couplings* (see Fig. 12 and 30). Further details on this matter are given in the section on cross-talk (6.4.1.).

1.3.3. Multiple twin quads (DM-quads)

Although the DM-quad (see 1.1.) with its phantom circuit is used in Germany on long-distance cable system (trunk cable system) now and before, its use abroad has been rarer. Wires of 0.8, 0.9 and 1.2 mm conductor diameter, insulated with paper string, are usual.

In the DM-quad wires are twisted to pairs and then two pairs are twisted together. However, to satisfy the requirements regarding cross-talk, explained in 6.4.1., the two pairs within the quad are subjected to a different amount of twist. The position of the two pairs, relative to one another is, therefore, continually changing. Fig. 13 shows the cross section through a DM-quad.

Although the thickness of the wires, and their mutual capacity is the same as in a star quad, the continually varying position of the pairs relative to one another gives the DM-quad a larger cross-section (see Fig. 13). Despite this increase of some 15%

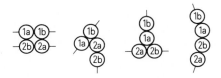

Fig. 13
Cross-sections of a DM-quad

23

in its cross-section, the DM-quad is always used for preference if its phantom line is to be used. The reason for this is that the ratio

$$\frac{C_{B\,phantom}}{C_{B\,side\,circuit}} \approx 1.6$$

is much more satisfactory than in the star quad (≈ 2.7). The line attenuation of the phantom circuit in the DM-quad is, consequently, lower than that of the phantom circuit in the star quad.

1.4. Unsymmetrical components (coaxial pairs)

Even when using the very latest insulating materials, the transmission range of symmetrical star quads is only sufficient for frequencies up to approximately 550 kHz. At this frequency, styroflex-insulated star quads are of course essential – to reduce the *leakage attenuation*. Where the wires of a star quad are insulated with paper "string" they can be used, for example, in CF systems with a maximum frequency of only some 250 kHz. At higher frequencies the attenuation of such cables increases so suddenly, due to *leakage losses*, that repeaters have to be used, located at very short intervals. Thus the economy of the transmission route can no longer be guaranteed. At even high-frequencies it becomes extremely difficult to maintain the required value of cross-talk attenuation – indeed it can only be achieved by very costly balancing methods.

The result of the increasing volume of telephone traffic, and the needs of the economy, which continually increases the immense variety of information to be transmitted, provides the demand for more and more transmission channels. For long-distance traffic this demand can only be satisfied, economically, by using the latest CF systems and cables with very wide bandwidths. Coaxial cables, which were once also known as broadband cables, are particularly suitable for this purpose. They are already used up to a frequency of 60 MHz.

A coaxial line (coaxial pair, also known as *tube*) consists basically of a cylindrical internal conductor surrounded by a hollow cylindrical external conductor. The central position of the internal conductor is maintained by an insulating material having a dielectric constant as low as possible.

Because there is a great difference in the electrical properties of the two conductors, for example, in their line-resistance and capacity to earth, a coaxial pair is considered to be an unsymmetrical line with respect to earth.

1.4.1. Coaxial pair for long-distance traffic

Even when coaxial cables were initially developed, paper was never used as the insulating material between the conductors, for the simple reason that the dissipation factor, tan δ, of paper is not satisfactory at high frequencies. The insulating material used in the earliest coaxial cables was styroflex, in the form of tapes, spirals and composite strings. The first, long, coaxial cable line in the world (300 km) was erected in Germany, in 1936, as a television line for the German "Reichspost". (Imperial Posts and Telegraphs) by AEG, Felten & Guilleaume (F & G) and Siemens. The diameter of the internal copper-conductor was 5 mm. The outer conductor, made by both F & G and Siemens, consisted of ten copper strips twisted in such a way that the hollow cylinder so produced had an internal diameter of 18 mm. The gaps between the strips of the external conductor were covered by a broader copper strip with a smaller lay. For the insulation between the internal and external conductor, both F & G and Siemens used a styroflex spiral. AEG however, instead of this, provided disc-shaped separators and made the external conductor of two copper strips, each bent to form a semicircle. Via this cable, television transmissions were made on a 2 MHz bandwidth and a CF system for audio transmission was operated respectively.

The coaxial cables normally used for CF transmission today are given in the recommendations of the International Telegraph and Telephone Consultative Committee (CCITT). They are:

the *standard coaxial pair*, 2.6/9.5 mm (or 0.104/0.375 in)

the *small diameter coaxial pair*, 1.2/4.4 mm (or 0.042/0.174 in).

The figures in front of the solidus (/) indicate the diameter of the internal conductor, and those after it the internal diameter of the external conductor.

From a consideration of the minimum conditions in the attenuation equation for coaxial pairs, the following ratio is obtained for a uniform dielectric and conductors made of the same material:

$$\frac{r_a}{r_i} \approx 3.6$$

where $2r_a$ is the internal diameter of the external conductor and $2r_i$ is the diameter of the internal conductor. The two previously-mentioned wide-band cables correspond to this ratio. This means that these cables have the optimal dimensions and, consequently, have the lowest attenuation constant.

In the standard 2.6/9.5 coaxial pair the concentricity of the internal conductor is maintained by polythene discs. Since tolerances thus produced, in relation to the permissible diameter of the internal conductor and the thickness of the tape that forms the external conductor, are sufficiently small to ensure that the longitudinal reflection (about 1%ₒ) is considerably smaller than the value recommended by CCITT (3%ₒ), the Siemens Company have also used this form of construction for their small diameter 1.2/4.4 coaxial pair.

Prior to the small diameter 1.2/4.4 coaxial pair being taken in the CCITT recommendations, the French firms had already developed their own technique which was somewhat different. A balloon (balloon-tube) of polythene is sprayed onto the internal conductor. The external diameter of this tube is approximately equal to the internal diameter of the external conductor, and to centre the internal conductor it is compressed at specified intervals against two sides of the internal conductor. As regards internal reflection, this design has a reflection factor also far below that of the maximum 5.5% recommended by CCITT for small diameter coaxial pairs 1.2/4.4.

In addition to this French design there are other small diameter coaxial pairs available which use a styroflex spiral to maintain the correct separation between the internal and external conductors. In England, for example, the insulation is in the form of two half-shells pressed together. In Japan it is in the form of a studded polythene-band.

Coaxial pairs with disc insulators are manufactured in principle as follows:

Polythene (PE) discs are sprayed onto the internal copper conductor with automatic spraying machines. On the standard coaxial pair (2.6/9.5), the distance between the discs is approximately 29 mm and on the small diameter coaxial pair (1.2/4.4) it is some 18 mm. The external conductor is formed, from a copper tape, into a tube by rolling. To obtain a proof voltage of 2 kV r.m.s., even on small diameter coaxial pair, a tape of styroflex is spun over the discs which thus lies beneath the external conductor. On the standard coaxial pair the separation between the internal and external conductor is itself sufficient. In both instances, however, two layers of a soft high-permeability steel tape are spun, as a covering, about the external conductors.

Without this covering the external conductor would be deformed if subjected to bending stresses. This covering also *screens* the coaxial pair with regard to cross-talk – this, actually, is its real purpose. In special instances the covering of steel tape is replaced by a covering of copper tapes, for example, in the DBP multi-cable 17a, which only has one standard coaxial pair and 8 styroflex insulated quads. Coaxial cables, in addition to the external metal tapes, have a covering of several layers of insulating material – usually of cable-insulating paper. Where a small diameter coaxial pair is required to be impermeable to lateral penetration (i.e., *waterresistant* from the external to the internal conductor), as is required, for example, by the German Federal Railways, then it has an external covering of insulation made of heavily overlapped plastics foils.

Where small diameter coaxial pairs are insulated with discs they are also largely impermeable longitudinally (i.e., water cannot pass along the coaxial pair) and, also in this respect, have the advantage over the *balloon tube*.

Cross-talk between coaxial pairs is highest at low frequencies and lessens as the frequency increases; or, to express this in another way, the cross-talk attenuation values are lowest at low frequencies. In the higher-frequency ranges they approach a limiting value, asymtotically. Consequently, coaxial cables are normally only used for carrier frequencies of 60 kHz or more.

The nominal value of the characteristic impedance[1] is 75 Ω, for standard coaxial pair, at a frequency of 2.5 MHz, and for small diameter coaxial pair at a frequency of 1 MHz.

The V300 and V960 carrier-frequency systems are operated with small diameter coaxial pairs at frequencies of 1.3 MHz and some 4 MHz, with nominal repeater sections of 8 km and 4 km.

For economic reasons the V300 system does not make use of standard coaxial pair. This is used for the V960 system (about 4 MHz with repeater sections nominally of 9 km), for TV systems (about 6 MHz, with repeater sections at 9 km spacing), for the V1260 system (about 5.5 MHz, 9 km), the V2700 system (12 MHz, 4.5 km), or for the V1200 + TV system (12 MHz, 4.5 km). It is also used already in the 60 MHz system for 10 800 channels, where the length of the repeater sections is approximately 1.5 km.

Note

The notation TV denotes one or several TV bandwidths in one direction; i.e., a single coaxial pair 2.6/9.5 is sufficient for such a transmission. In the four-wire system (V), two coaxial pairs are required for each audio direction. The figures after the V indicate the number of audio channels, at a frequency band of 300 to 3400 Hz. Thus, V2700 means that 2700 conversations can be carried on simultaneously, over two coaxial pairs 2.6/9.5.

1.4.2. Coaxial cable for high frequency transmission

Although *high-frequency coaxial cables* have no components or stranding elements, since they can only be treated as a complete cable, it is worth-while including them in this discussion.

When transmitting power at high frequencies, in the range up to some 11 GHz, whether from the transmitter to the antenna or from the antenna to the receiver, it is only necessary to cover short distances (at most, some hundreds of meters). Because of their reliability in operation and their good electrical properties, HF coaxial cables are used. These cables are also required for the HF connections between the various units in an installation.

In contrast to coaxial pairs for CF systems, HF cables always have to transmit large quantities of power. Whether these cables are insulated with discs or with plastics-

---

[1] line characteristic, see 6.1

spirals, their power losses are relatively small; all these cables are noted for their low attenuation and their high electrical integrity. The low attenuation is due to the small amount of insulating material between the internal and external conductors, and the highly satisfactory dielectric constant thus produced.

Where the nominal value of the external conductor is 40 mm or more, HF cables can be protected with special flat-wire armouring to withstand the tensile forces which occur when the cable is vertically arranged. A protective covering of plastics, normally of polythene, forms the external sealing of the cable.

The characteristic impedance of the HF cables used in German was 60 Ω but the types mainly used abroad have a characteristic impedance of 50 Ω. HF cables with a characteristic impedance of 75 Ω will also be used in future.

2. Cable design

The cables specified in VDE 0816 as outdoor cables for communications installations are constructed with the symmetrical components (stranding elements) quoted in Chapter 1, and are used predominantly for the connections between communications equipment installed in separate buildings.

Depending on the engineering requirements, VDE 0816 distinguishes between the following types of outdoor cables:

(a) Signal and metering cable

(b) Subscriber cables (cables for local networks)
    Long-range telephone cables

(c) Signal and telephone cables for underground use in mines.

These types of cables are ordered according to VDE 0816 (Specifications) by German-based clients. In certain instances, special conditions which deviate from this specification may be agreed upon. When the conditions of VDE 0816 are not applicable, or only partially so, special specifications are supplied by the customer, sometimes in full agreement with the manufacturer. To such special cables belong long-distance cables with star-quads for CF transmission and/or coaxial pairs, submarine cables, ships or naval cables, HF cables and other special types. Those cables manufactured for customers abroad are also frequently made to different specifications.

A communications cable always comprises a *cable core* and *cable sheath*. Depending on the materials used, and upon the operational stresses to which they may be subjected, or for external indication/identification purposes the cable may sometimes also be covered with protective sheathings. For various reasons communications cables are also provided with armouring which is generally arranged beneath a protective sheathing.

The stranding elements are wires, pairs, star and DM-quads, and coaxial pairs.

The cable sheath, the protective sheathing (where it is provided) and the armouring are intended to prevent moisture penetrating into the cable core, and to provide protection against mechanical stresses and electrical interference.

2.1. The cable core

In a communications cable all the stranding elements, including the wrapping of the cable core, or inner sheath, are considered to be part of the cable core.

In the stranding of a cable core two fundamentally-different methods of production have to be distinguished:

(a) *stranding in layers* and

(b) *stranding in units* (bunches)

When a cable is stranded in layers the individual strands in the external cable are arranged in concentric layers. When a cable is stranded in units it comprises several units each of which contain several strands (Fig. 14).

Starting from a marking element (an item, such as a pair of wires, to show where to commence enumerating the wires, usually identified by a red-*coloured spiral*) then, if the construction of the wires is identical in both directions, if the marking of the strands is the same and if the groups of strands are identically arranged, such out-door cables are known as symmetrically designed cables.

All cables of differing construction are known as unsymmetrical designed cables. In addition to the marking elements they also incorporate direction indicators. When looking at the cable end, if the direction indicator appears to be turning clockwise, adjacent to the marking unit, then this is the start (A-end) of the cable (see VDE 0816, para. 13).

When cables are stranded in units as the definition suggests, it is only the units which are counted. In this instance the term used is symmetrical construction and, consequently, the A-end (start) of the cable can be determined at either end.

When cables are stranded in units they are always made with the same type of strands (identical dimensions for the conductors, wires, or star quads). When cables are stranded in layers they can be manufactured with different combinations of strands such as, for example, long-range cables containing, coaxial pairs, star quads, symmetrical pairs, and single wires. For economy, an effort must always be made to maintain the cable-core diameter as small as possible, and to combine the separate strands in such a way that they produce a satisfactory cable make-up. Costly thickening of the strands or *dummies* (or *fillers*) should be avoided.

 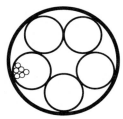

Fig. 14   Stranding in layers (left), and in units

Special care should be taken to ensure, so far as possible, that subscriber cables and long distance telephone cables contain uniform strands.

2.1.1. Stranding in layers

The separate strands are arranged in concentric layers around the cable axis. With the exception of the 1 + 6 arrangement, the number of strands in each successive layer increases by six. This, of course, assumes that the strands are all of the same diameter (see Table 1).

To produce a cable where the strands are multiples of ten, it is frequently necessary to depart from this basic sheme. In such instances steps of five or seven strands are required.

The centre of the cable core, even if it only contains a single strand is, on principle, denoted as the first layer (VDE definition).

Where the strands are of uniform dimensions and are arranged in the conal geometrical pattern, then cable cores can be constructed with, for example, star quads in the various different ways noted in Table 1.

Each layer has its own amount of twist which differs from that of the neighbouring layers. The length of twist is the pitch of a helical line after it has turned through 360° (Fig. 15).

To give the cable its maximum flexibility, and to provide satisfactory *electrical decoupling* between the strands of the separate layers, it is necessary to twist each layer. Moreover, the length of the twist is selected to ensure that the cables will bend properly. If the layers were not twisted, the cable would behave like a solid cylinder.

When stranding the core on a standard production length of cable, it is also important whether a counter rotation is or is not given to the strands. If, when the strands come off the drums, the axis of the drums are determined in the carriage of the stranding machine, then there is no counter rotation in the stranding. Each strand thus receives an additional amount of twist equivalent to the twist length. If the actual twist of the strand (e.g. twist of a star quad), and the twist given to the layer, is in the same direction then the twisting of the element becomes tighter.

Layer	1	2	3	4	...
Number of strands per layer	1	6	12	18	...
	2	8	14	20	...
	3	9	15	21	...
	4	10	16	22	...
	5	11	17	23	...

Table 1
Various ways of arranging star quads in a cable core

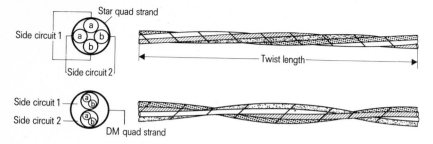

Fig. 15 Length of twist on star quads (above) and DM-quads

Where the twists are in opposite directions there is a tendency for untwisting of the strands.

When cables are stranded with a counter rotation the drums used on the shaft of the stranding machine rotate at the same angular velocity as the carriage of the stranding machine, but turn in the opposite direction. The strands therefore run off the drums without any torsion. To avoid faults, or damage due to torsion, coaxial pairs are, on principle, stranded with a counter rotation.

2.1.2. Stranding in units

The method of unit stranding used in Germany is only one of the many possible methods of bunching cables. At present, bunched cables are manufactured both with plastics insulation (solid or cellular polythene-PE) and also with paper-insulated strands.

The *basic unit* has ten pairs and contains five star quads which are all stranded with same twist.

Fig. 16 The basic unit

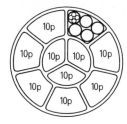

Fig. 17   Main units of 50 and 100 pairs

The *main units*, made from the basic units, either have 50 or 100 pairs, comprising five basic units each having five star quads, or ten basic units each of which has five star quads. The basic units are stranded together to form the main unit. During the stranding process it is important to see that the units intended to form the cable are properly shaped as shown, ideally, in Fig. 17.

When cable cores have more than 100 pairs they are made from main units of 50 or 100 pairs. Cables of up to 500 pairs are made from 50-pair main units; cables with 600 to 2000 pairs being made from 100-pair main units.

Exceptions to this rule are cables with 0.8 and 0.9 mm diameter conductors which are made from 50-pair main units, even when the cable has as many as 500 or 800 pairs.

The bunched arrangement of cables has advantages when installed in subscriber networks, where numerous cable branchings are generally essential. Moreover, with plastics-insulated cables, it is also possible to bring the basic and main units directly to the main distributor in the exchange i.e., without any splicing. But, in such instances, the units must only be carried in PVC tubing or in some corresponding material.

Besides plastics-insulated unit type cables, unit cables are also manufactured abroad with paper-insulated conductors, the units may also be designed in separate layers.

Straw-rope stranding is a method of stranding unit cables solely used abroad. It is only used for paper-insulated cables, and all the strands in a unit have the same twist.

2.1.3. The core wrapping

The purpose of the core wrapping is to hold the strands in the cable core together, for the subsequent stages in their processing, to prevent damage to the wires during subsequent manufacturing processes and to provide the necessary dielectric strength

33

against the screen (e.g., a copper-tape wrapping) and the metal sheathing. In special circumstances the wrapping on the core also acts as an insulating thermal screen when fitting the sheath.

The material used for the core wrapping depends on the type of cable. It is advisable, for example, to provide paper-insulated cables with a wrapping of paper-tapes. The wall thickness, necessary for core wrapping, is given in VDE 08 16.

Aluminium sheathed cables have a fairly-thick wrapping (heat-insulating layers).

Because the relatively high line-resistance of the corrugated-steel sheath is not usually sufficient to protect the cable from external electrical interference, an additional metal screen has to be provided over the cable core wrapping. Cables operated at low-frequency (not subscriber cables) have a metal-covered paper screen. Cables containing CF star-quads or coaxial pairs are screened with a layer of aluminium or copper tape.

Cables whose conductors are insulated with plastics usually have an external plastics sheath. The wrapping for the cable core is made from several layers of plastics foil and/or in special instances, of an inner plastics sheath.

2.1.4. Markings

Cables for external communications installations, according to VDE 0816, are required to carry *coloured tracer-threads*, registered as a trade mark of the particular manufacturing firm. This coloured tracer-thread is generally laid, longitudinally, directly under the core wrapping when the cable is stranded. Siemens divide this thread into sections in the following sequence: green, white, red, white. The length of the sections is changed every year so that the date of manufacture of a cable can always be determined.

In addition to the manufacturer's tracer thread, a *VDE tracer thread* is also included if the cable satisfies the conditions of the VDE specification, and if it has received the approval of the VDE Testing Board. These tracers have alternate, 10 mm-long, red- and black-coloured bands.

Cables supplied to foreign countries frequently have an additional strip of paper, inserted between the core wrapping, on which is displayed the manufacturer's name, date of manufacture and any special data requested by the customer.

Many customers, including the DBP, require the insertion of a paper measuring-tape. A 6 mm-wide paper strip, with meter divisions continuously printed along it is used for this purpose. Although not sufficiently accurate to serve as an exact measurement of the cable length, for many on-site activities such as, for example, the cutting of the gauge lengths when laying the cable, the accuracy of this measuring tape is quite sufficient.

2.2. The cable sheaths

Within certain limits the cable sheath will prevent any damage to the cable core due to the effects of external mechanical stress and, depending on the type of material used, it can also play a very considerable part in protecting the cable core from external electrical interference.

Provided that the sheath suffers no permanent damage resulting from excessive stressing during laying or as a result of subsequent constructional work, it can also provide substantial protection against external chemical action and the impermissible effects of moisture. With very few exceptions cables with plastic sheaths, when used for communications plants have an aluminium- or copper-tape (or foil) screen inserted between the core wrapping and the outer sheathing, or between the sheaths themselves.

Where there are no special requirements relative to a *gas pressure supervisory* in a cable installation, the sheath should encompass the cable core as tightly as possible.

Hydraulically-operated sheathing presses can apply lead, and sometimes aluminium sheaths evenly and flush onto the cable core. Metal sheaths are also produced from steel and aluminium tapes. A rolling machine shapes these tapes into cylindrical forms, and the longitudinal seam is then welded. In such instances the internal diameter of the tube is, at first, larger by a specified amount than the external diameter of the cable core. In a subsequent process this tube is shaped into a so-called *corrugated sheath*, by the pressure of an endless-spiral with a very short pitch and correspondingly deep troughs, which make contact with the cable core. At the present time aluminium sheaths, first produced in a sufficiently wide press, are also being shaped into corrugated sheaths by a similar process.

In Germany the following process, as specified in VDE 0472/9.71, is usually adopted to determine the wall thickness of, for example, a smooth metal sheath (not a corrugated sheath or a screen):

From each end of a manufactured length of cable, a piece of the sheathing (about 5 cm long) is removed. It is then split longitudinally, and flattened and cleaned without altering its wall-thickness. Five micrometer measurements are then made on each piece of sheathing. These measurements are equally-distributed about the perimeter of the sheathing, and must be at least 10 mm from each edge. The average value of the ten measurements gives the wall thickness of the lead sheathing.

Where the conductors of communications cables are insulated with plastics, the cable sheath is usually also of plastics. PE is lighter than the usual cable-sheath materials. Moreover, plastics are not subject to corrosion, and have an exceptionally-high dynamic strength. Plastic-covered cables have another advantage; their low weight reduces the cost of packaging and transport. This reduction in weight generally reduces the number of problems that occur during the cable-laying process. Plastic cables can, generally, also be used for *conduit cable* and *buried cable*. It is thus more practical to hold such cable in store as a reserve cable. By virtue of its low weight, in comparison with metal-sheathed cables, and when used as conduit cable, it is usually possible to install twice the length of a section with a single standard-production length. The result is a considerable saving in the number of connecting accessories and installation costs.

Where reliability of operation is the most important factor (for instance, in cables for pipe-lines, or for the control of public water supplies etc.), then the use of cables with solid PE-insulation on communications cable connections is a guarantee, even when the cable core may become permeated with moisture due to some slight damage of the cable, that the flow of information will not be interrupted, as happens with paper-insulated cables without gas pressure supervisory. For such cable connections continuously-filled PE cables with laminated sheaths have recently been used since the operational reliability of the cable installation is hereby even further improved.

Plastics sheaths are applied to the cable cores by *extrusion methods*. More precise details on plastics are given in 1.1.2.

2.2.1. Lead sheath

To manufacture lead sheaths, cable lead is used with or without the addition of copper (DIN 17640). In case of higher dynamic stresses when a cable is in operation, the lead for the cable sheath must have additions of antimony or tellurium, as hardeners. An additive to harden the lead sheath is required, simply to enable it to withstand the shaking to which it is subjected during transport for example, when it is sent overseas. Overseas, antimony-alloyed lead sheaths are often preferred. For buried cables an alloy of tellurium is the most satisfactory or, rather, is an advantage because of its properties (principally, its intercrystalline stability). Abroad antimony alloyed lead sheaths are considered to be particularly corrosion-resistant.

In Germany these alloys usually contain 0.04% tellurium or 0.5% antimony (VDE 0816). Abroad, a higher percentage of antimony is required; on average, 0.8%.

When it is pressed onto the cable core the lead sheath attains a temperature of some 200°C. The nominal value for the wall-thickness of the lead sheath in Germany, which depends on the application (and design) of the cable and on the thickness of the core beneath the sheathing, lies, according to VDE 0816, between 1.3 and 3.2 mm.

The *reduction factor* is a value which indicates the extent to which metal sheaths can protect the cable core from external inductive and ohmic interference. For an unarmoured, lead-sheathed cable this value is approximately 0.9. This value is unsatisfactory, i.e., unless additional precautions are taken, such cables are not suitable where there is a large amount of electrical interference.

36

2.2.2. Aluminium sheath

It was Siemens who first succeded, some thirty years ago, in pressing an aluminium sheath around a cable core.

The aluminium used to manufacture cable sheaths in Germany must have a purity of at least 99.5% (DIN 1712).

When aluminium is being pressed into a smooth cable sheath it reaches a temperature of 450 °C (guiding value). Additional heat-insulation is therefore required on the core wrapping (see 2.1.3.) to protect the cable core from the effects of excessive heat.

In Germany too, according to VDE 0816, the wall thickness of a smooth aluminium sheath, depending on the diameter beneath the sheath, is between 0.9 and 1.4 mm. Corrugated aluminium sheaths on the basis of smooth aluminium tubes are manufactured where the diameter under the corrugated sheathing is 40 mm or more.

The nominal value for the wall thickness of aluminium-tape corrugated sheath is between 0.5 and 1.5 mm (VDE 0816), depending on the diameter beneath the sheathing.

A thin, superficial, layer of oxide forms over any clean aluminium surface. This frequently prevents any further oxidization. When a clean aluminium surface is laid in the earth, however, this layer of oxide is continually being removed by mechanical action, and is therefore continually being renewed with the result that, in the course of time, the aluminium distintegrates.

Alkaline substances and dissolved salts in the earth also *corrode* aluminium. Consequently, aluminium sheaths must always be surrounded by a bitumen protective layer having good bonding properties, and a further protective sheath to prevent the corrosion and mechanical destruction of the protective layer.

In contrast with lead sheaths, the reduction factor of the aluminium sheath is very good, amounting to about 0.3 or 0.4. By including armouring to provide protection against inductive interference, reduction factors of the order of 0.1 can be obtained. Thus, cables with aluminium sheaths are especially suitable where exists severe electrical interference.

2.2.3. Corrugated-steel sheath

Corrugated-steel sheaths are manufactured, in Germany, from steel tape having a nominal wall-thickness of between 0.3 and 0.6 mm (VDE 0816). The thickness of the tape depends on the diameter beneath the sheath.

The corrugation of the steel tape is the condition so that the cable can be bent without deforming the cable core. Corrugated-steel sheaths must have an external covering applied directly to the metal sheath, because steel, unlike aluminium, when subjected to moisture will rust without forming any anti-corrosion layer. It is, consequently, advisable when using cable with corrugated-steel sheath to provide additional gas-pressure supervising. If the sheath of the cable becomes damaged, the excess internal pressure of the dry gas will normally prevent the penetration of any moisture into the cable core.

Because the electrical line-resistance of the corrugated-steel sheath is greater than that of the lead sheath, the reduction factor of the corrugated-steel sheath is even more unsatisfactory. High-quality VF-cables, and cables with CF star quads and coaxial pairs are, therefore, fitted with a screen beneath the sheath. This screen may be metal-covered paper, aluminium tape, copper tape or a layer of aluminium or copper wires.

2.2.4. PVC sheath

On external-used cables, PVC sheaths are only provided for signal and metering cables and for mining cables. Indoor cables usually have a PVC sheath. Outdoor cables, using PVC, usually have no screening beneath the sheath.

In Germany, the nominal value of the wall thickness of the sheath, depending on the type of cable and the diameter beneath the sheath, is between 1.4 mm and 4.0 mm (VDE 0816).

PVC sheaths can be made largely oil-resistant, so that they are suitable for pipe-line projects.

In Germany, PVC sheaths without following component have different colours,

blue: installations which are intrinsically-safe in mines and in undertakings where there is danger of explosions;

grey: communications installations for power supplies and industrial plant (including underground mines);

black: for all other outdoor communications cables.

The surface of PVC feels slightly rough. Jointing sleeves for cables with a PVC sheathing are usually made from a casting resin (e.g., PROTOLIN® 19 or 51), which is cast in special shapes (frictional connection process).

2.2.5. PE sheath

With only a few exceptions, cables with PE sheaths are always fitted with a screen beneath the external sheathing. This screen is of aluminium or copper tape or foil. As in metal-sheathed cables, the screen performs various functions. It protects the cable staticly from the effects of externa electric fields and, if only to a limited extent, reduces the effects of external electrical interference (whether inductive or ohmic). The reduction factor is, on average, about 0.9, just as for lead-sheathed cables of the same diameter. If there is higher electrical interference then different types of cable, e.g., with an aluminium sheath, are to be provided. The screen helps stabilise the transmission characteristics of the cable, and acts as a return path in simple cable connections which are not operated symmetrically to earth. Aluminium screens are usually 0.2 mm thick, and copper screens usually 0.12 mm thick. They can be fitted smoothly to cables with up to 17 mm diameter cores. Where the cable-core diameter is larger the screens can be grooved.

Under "normal" lightning conditions cables with plastics sheaths (but without an inner sheath) are not as satisfactory as those with an inner sheath since the electric strength between the conductor and screen is not as high. Where lightning is very frequent it is necessary to use earthed cables i.e., cables having an external armouring of bare, round or flat, wire.

Sheaths have recently been designed as *laminated sheaths*, where an aluminium tape some 0.2 mm thick is covered on both sides with a layer of plastics. The aluminium tape is shaped into a tube by rolling machines, which give the tape a sufficient overlap. The PE sheath, which is subsequently applied, attaches itself to the outer plastics covering on the tape as a result of the heat produced during the manufacturing process and also welds the overlapping points. The internal plastics layer on the Al tape also protects the aluminium against corrosion. Because it acts as a barrier to permeation by water vapour, this laminated sheath is very suitable for sheathing strands insulated with paper or cellular PE.

Depending on the diameter below the sheath the nominal wall thickness of the external sheath in Germany is between 1.8 and 4.0 mm (VDE 0816).

Natural-coloured PE is not resistant to the prolonged effects of ultra-violet radiation. Some 2% of lamp black is therefore mixed with PE when processing it for sheathing. PE sheathing is, therefore, always black. Consequently, for intrinsically-safe installations such as power supply and industrial plant it is not suitable unless it has a coloured protective covering of PVC over the PE sheath.

The surface of PE has a slightly slippery feeling.

PE can not be bonded with the help of adhesives. When heat and pressure are simultaneously applied the bonding of PE is so strong that it will withstand all operating stresses (even when the cable is gas pressure supervised). To connect cables insulated and sheathed with PE, Siemens, in collaboration with Felten and Guilleaume, have developed an electrical welding process, by which the PE sheath can be bonded to the PE sleeve, largely without depending on the skill and experience of the fitter since the two are connected together by fusion (an interlocking process). Continuously-filled PE cables for external use, can also be connected together by an appropiate frictional force locking process, e.g., with a screw-type clamping sleeve.

2.3. Protective coverings

The purpose of protective coverings on cables is to substantially protect the metal sheathing and any armouring that may be provided from excessive corrosion. VDE 0816 contains details on the various types of protective coverings with their appropriate applications.

For example, conduit cables with lead sheaths, where they are peculiarly liable to corrosion under operating conditions, are provided with an extra anti-corrosive covering (e.g., bitumen) which is then covered with a protective layer of PE or PVC.

Armoured cables usually have an inner and outer protective covering. The inner protective covering has a bolstering effect; it protects the cable from damage while it is being armoured. When the sheath is a metal one the inner protective covering also provides protection from corrosion. The outer protective covering safeguards the armouring against corrosion.

The internal and external protective coverings are usually made from a combination of substances (where bitumen is used it must contain no phenols) such as, for example, rubber or plastic foils, fibres and plastics. The external protective covering is usually sealed with impregnated jute, and an over-layer of non-adhesive chalk, or is of plastics.

Plastics protective coverings are increasingly being made of PE. Where, for instance, oil-resistant protective coverings or coloured coverings are an essential or an advantage, in Germany PVC protective coverings are furthermore provided.

2.4. Armouring

The *armouring* of a communications cable protects the cable core and the sheath from mechanical stresses. Special types of armouring can improve the cable reduction factor relative to electrical interference.

Depending on the cable design and its application the armouring is made of *steel tape* and *flat* or *round wire*.

Steel tape armouring is usually made from two steel tapes. The thickness of the tape, which depends on the diameter beneath the cable sheath, is, in Germany, 0.5, 0.8 or 1.0 mm. The gaps between the turns of a layer of steel tape may not be greater than one third the width of the tape (VDE 08 16). The upper layer of steel tape must adequately overlap the space between the turns of the lower tapes on both of its sides. Cables armoured with steel tape must not be subjected to tensile stresses and are therefore only used as buried cable. They can not be used for conduit cable due to the tensile stress when being drawn into the conduit.

For certain types of cables laid in the ground, for cables in mines and cables subject to tensile stress, only wire armouring is used. Flat wire must not have sharp edges. According to VDE 0816, its thickness, depending on the diameter under the cable sheath may be 0.8, 1.2 or 1.4 mm. Where the cable diameter under the sheath is not more than 10 mm the round wire used in Germany is 1.4 mm diameter. Where the cables are subjected to greater stresses (self-supporting overhead cable, mine-shaft cabling, river cables and shallow water cables), particularly where the cable diameter underneath the sheathing is large, they are armoured with thicker wires to suit the maximum stress. The armouring wires (flat or round) must lock tightly together.

On all cables in mines, and on cables which have no external protective covering, the armouring must be heavily galvanized. If a contra-wound spiral of steel tape, not less than 0.3 mm thick, is provided or required in the specification (mine cables) for wire armoured cables, then this must also be as heavily galvanized as the armouring beneath it to prevent corrosion (electrolytic formation). Untwisting of the armouring is prevented by the counter-spiral. The anti-inductive interference armouring, necessary to improve the cable reduction factor, is usually made of standard commercial steel tapes.

In special instances, where inductive interference from electric fields of particularly high strength has to be taken into consideration the reduction factor required in this range can be achieved by providing an additional covering of flat wire over the steel tape armouring.

Where a communications cable is subject to considerable danger from ligthning it is provided with a heavily-galvanized-wire armouring (usually, round wire) which seals the cable externally. This cable without an external protective covering has contact to earth immediately and can conduct the lightning currents rapidly to earth.

Plastic-covered cables are usually laid in the ground or in conduit without any armouring. There are, however, exceptions, where armouring is provided, if high stress during the laying of the cable are inevitable, as for instance heavy constructional work when building pipe-lines, or if exceptionally-high tensile or compressive loads have to be taken into consideration (for example cables layed on mountain slopes).

Signal cables for railway administrations with PVC sheath are provided with a so called spare armouring, consisting of a layer of 0.3 mm thick steel tape covered with compound. The gaps between the turns must not be more than 2 mm. Between the plastics sheath and the tape armouring there is at least one protective layer of impregnated fibruous tape and viscous compound.

VDE 0816 gives more precise details on the subject of armouring.

2.5. Types of communications cables

Although there are a larger variety of possible cable designs the outdoor communications cables discussed here are the basic types available. Hence, the text only explains the special characteristics and possible applications of these cables. Further details can be obtained, with the exception of long-distance cables, from VDE 0816.

Outdoor communications cables can be divided into two groups: namely, *signal* or *metering cables* and *telephone cables*. Although there are no problems with the first group of cables, sometimes very numerous, strict and predominantly electrical demands are made of telephone cables for subscriber, main switchboard cables and cables for long-distance operation.

2.5.1. Signal and metering cables

Signal and metering cables (VDE 0816, Table 1) are predominantly used for the transmission of d.c. and low-frequency a.c. in clock, telemetry, monitoring, call-ringing, and signalling installations as well as for control purposes.

Signal and metering cables are not subject to any requirements regarding attenuation. Their operating range depends on the cross-section of the conductors and the operating voltage i.e., the permissible voltage drop. Only copper conductors are used, 0.9, 1.4 and 1.8 mm diameter. At a temperature of 20 °C these conductors have a maximum conductor resistance of 28.9, 11.9 and 7.2 Ω/km. VDE 0816 allows an operating (peak) voltage of 600 V.

Until a few years ago the conductor insulation was an impregnated paper, rubber or PVC. Today, only PE is used for insulation.

The cables are formed from single wires stranded in layers. The wires are coloured grey. The pilot wire for each of the layers is blue.

The *insulation resistance* has to satisfy the operating requirements and the cable construction; at a temperature of 20 °C it is at least 5000 M$\Omega \cdot$ km, for PE wires. The wire-to-wire, or wire-to-sheath test voltage must be 2500 V r.m.s. Maximum values for the mutual capacitance are also specified.

The cable sheath can be of lead or aluminium (smooth or corrugated). Corrugated steel sheaths are also sometimes used. Today the sheath is generally made of plastic (PVC).

2.5.2. Cables for local networks (subscriber cables)

The concept of a *local cable*, (VDE 0816 Table 2) is very closely associated with the DBP telephone network. With the few exceptions of the electrical communications network on the German Federal Railways, and on the German motorway and water-way systems, for example, the DBP has a monopoly of the telephone system. Besides the above-mentioned traffic operators, which are also quoted in the Government Act on communications installations, the following, which are private communications installations within the meaning of Paragraph 3 of this Act, can be operated without official authorisation:

(a) installations operated by the country, local or municipal authorities, or communal associations such as the corporations in charge of dykes, drainage, and sluices, insofar as these installations are exclusively confined to these services

(b) installations operated by transport establishments along their own lines, for their own exclusive use (tramways belong to this class)

(c) installations within the confines of a private estate or private premises, even if the installations are used – with or without payment – by third parties

(d) installations shared between several private premises belonging to one owner (proprietor within the meaning of the German Civil Code), or considered to be parts of a single concern, where the longest distance between the properties is not more than 25 km, and where such installations are exclusively intended for non-profit making telephone traffic associated with the use of these properties.

Other communications installations such as those of the electricity supply concerns must apply for the Official authorisation of the DBP. This is not always given for private telecommunications plants.

Subscriber cables in the DBP are intended to connect the subscriber to the *local exchange* and in such instances are known as *local exchange connection cables*. Subscriber cables are also used to connect together the local exchanges in a local network, and are then known as *local exchange connecting cables*. The local network, which includes the connections of the subscribers cables to the local exchanges and the connections between the local exchanges, is the lower-level network.

In the DBP the local connection cables are known as *main cables* if they provide the connections between the equipment in the local exchanges and the cable distributing equipment (switch points such as cable distribution boxes). *Branch cables* are, however, local connection cables by means of which the distributing equipment and the *terminal equipment* (e.g. terminal boxes) or the local exchanges, in the neighbourhood of local exchanges or local networks operated without cable distributors (fixed networks), can be directly connected to their terminal equipments.

Note

The following are special concepts of the DBP.

For the cable strands, use is principally made of St III star quads (see 1.3.2.). The two side circuits in the star quad of the cable are each generally allotted a single audio-frequency band (usually 0.3 to 3.4 kHz). The values for the reference equivalent between the subscriber and the local exchange, quoted in the DBP attenuation plan 55, must be observed. Account has to be taken of the fact that the operating range (length) of the local connection cable (subscriber cable) very considerably depends on the loop resistance of the main line. *Coil-loading* is only provided for a part of cables where the copper conductors have diameters of 0.6 and 0.8 mm.

Where the length of the local connection cable is 3.5 km or less, the diameter of the copper conductor is 0.4 mm; in excess of this length it is 0.6 mm. By improvements in the reproduction properties of microphones and in the subscriber's equipment, and by means of modern selector-dialling systems, conductors of 0.4 mm diameter can be used on even longer sections.

The local connection cables in use which are stranded in layers, may be paper-insulated with metal sheaths or may be insulated with solid PE and have a laminated PE sheath. These may be fully filled (distributing cables) or not filled (main cables).

The cables which make the connections between local exchanges usually contain St III star quads with copper conductors of either, 0.6 or 0.8 mm diameter, and St I star quads with 0.9 mm diameter copper conductors. In addition to the cables with paper "string" insulated star quads, stranded in layers, and covered with a metal sheath, increasing use is being made of unfilled cables containing conductors insulated with cellular PE, stranded in units and with laminated PE sheath. Local connecting cables are generally coil-loaded.

Subscriber cables are used as station communication cables on the German Federal Railways system, and are also the cables most frequently required by private customers.

The electrical properties of the delivery lengths of St III subscriber cables are specified in VDE 08 16 for a temperature of 20 °C.

(a) Insulation-resistance of insulated cables, delivery length more than 200 m: at least 5000 MΩ · km

(b) Test voltage between wires for paper-or PE-insulated wires: 500 V r.m.s. (with the exception of paperinsulated wires with copper conductors of 0.4 mm diameter)

(c) Test voltage between wire and sheath or screen for every type of wire: 2000 V r.m.s.

The maximum *operating voltage* (peak value) for 0.4 mm conductors is 150 V, but may be 225 V for 0.6 and 0.8 mm conductors.

The maximum *loop resistance* per km (the resistance of the two conductors in a main line) is:

300 Ω, for 0.4 mm diameter conductors
130 Ω, for 0.6 mm diameter conductors and
73.2 Ω, for 0.8 mm diameter conductors.

For 100% of all the values the maximum *mutual capacity* of a side circuit per km may be:

for paper-insulated conductors

0.4 mm conductor diameter	38 nF
0.6 mm conductor diameter	} 42 nF
0.8 mm conductor diameter	

for solid PE-insulated conductors

0.4 mm conductor diameter	50 nF
0.6 mm conductor diameter	52 nF
0.8 mm conductor diameter	55 nF

for cellular PE-insulated conductors

0.6 mm and	} 42 nF
0.8 mm conductor diameter	

Additional differences are specified in VDE 0816, Table 2. At a frequency of 800 Hz the *line attenuation* (planning value) per km of a side circuit is approximately;

for paper-insulated conductors

0.4 mm conductor diameter	1.30 dB	(150 mNp)
0.6 mm conductor diameter	0.91 dB	(105 mNp)
0.8 mm conductor diameter	0.70 dB	(80 mNp)

for solid PE-insulated conductors

0.4 mm conductor diameter	1.49 dB	(172 mNp)
0.6 mm conductor diameter	1.04 dB	(120 mNp)
0.8 mm conductor diameter	0.78 dB	(90 mNp)

for cellular PE-insulated conductors

0.6 mm conductor diameter	0.91 dB	(105 mNp)
0.8 mm conductor diameter	0.70 dB	(80 mNp).

For all conductor diameters and types of insulation the *capacitive couplings*, at a frequency of 800 Hz and a reference length of 300 m, must not be greater than:

k_1 400 pF
$k_{9\ldots12}$ 300 pF
$e_{1.2}$ 800 pF.

Up to 2% (but at least two values) of all the k_1 values of a cable may be up to 800 pF (reference length 300 m).

Paper-insulated subscriber cables (St III)

The local (subscriber) cables at present supplied to the DBP with paper insulated conductors, contain star quads as the stranding elements, and are stranded in layers or in units. The diameter of the conductors may be 0.4, 0.6 or 0.8 mm. Until a few years ago conductors insulated with paper "string" were permitted. Recently, 0.4 mm diameter conductors have been used as tubular wires.

When these paper-insulated cables were used by private customers they had to satisfy basically the same conditions as the cables for the DBP.

Marking of wires and method of enumerating cables stranded in layers:

The natural-coloured external paper tape on wire 1 b, 2 a, and 2 b on every star quad has a blue- or black-coloured strip printed across it in such a way that, when the wires are finally processed, they are marking rings as shown in Fig. 18.

To provide a *marker* for each layer, the external paper tape on the a-wire of side circuit 1 is coloured red.

Since such cables are symmetrically designed, no direction marker is required. By marking each of the wires, and by marking a specified star quad as a pilot marker for the star quads in each layer, any side circuit within the cable can be unambiguously identified. The usual practice is to count the strands in pairs, continuously, from inside to outside.

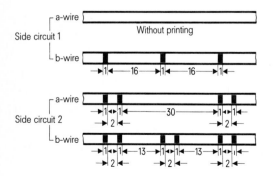

Fig. 18
Marking the wires on
paper insulated conductors
stranded in layers

The notation for paper-insulated cable stranded in units corresponds to that for PE-insulated cables stranded in units. In this instance natural-coloured paper is used instead of the white-coloured wire covering. Steel tape (corrugated sheeths), lead, and sometimes also aluminium are used as sheathing materials.

PE-insulated subscriber cables (St III)

Plastics-insulated cables can be produced with star quads, where the conductors are insulated with either solid or cellular PE and are stranded in layers or in units.

The DBP uses plastics-insulated cables for the connections between local exchanges; these cables are supervised (as are the paper insulated cables used for this purpose) by pressure-gas. Cellular PE is used to insulate the conductors, and the cable core is stranded in units. The diameter of the conductors may be 0.6, 0.8 or 0.9 mm. The cable core is protected by a laminated sheath (see 2.2.5.). Furthermore, the DBP uses plastics-insulated cables as local connection cable in the main cable system at present. These cables are then insulated with solid PE, have conductors 0.4 mm diameter, are stranded in units and are surrounded with a laminated sheath.

For branch-line cabling the DBP will, in future, only provide continuously-filled cable, with laminated sheath which contains 0.4 or 0.6 mm diameter conductors insulated with solid PE and stranded in units.

Where a cable is stranded in layers, the insulation covering of the conductors of each star quad is coloured:

side circuit 1	a-wire:	yellow
	b-wire:	red
side circuit 2	a-wire:	green
	b-wire:	blue

The pilot marker for each layer is indicated by an open spiral made of red-coloured PE tape or threads. Since the cable is symmetrically designed, no directional marker is required.

When a cable is stranded in units, the insulation coverings of the conductors in each of the basic units, which always contain five star quads, have the following different colours:

red:	for the insulation of all the wires in star quad 1
green:	for the insulation of all the wires in star quad 2
grey:	for the insulation of all the wires in star quad 3
yellow:	for the insulation of all the wires in star quad 4
white:	for the insulation of all the wires in star quad 5

47

In addition, the wires in each of the star quads are marked with rings (Fig. 18), on the same principle as these of paperinsulated quads. The rings are applied with blue-coloured or black-coloured indelible dyes.

With the exception of the marker unit in each layer, which has a red-coloured marking spiral, the basic and main units (see 2.1.2.) have white, open spirals as markers. These spirals are made of PE tape or some similar material.

By this method of marking and grouping the star quads in units, the installation of units cables can be more efficiently done than it is for cables stranded in layers.

Subscriber cables abroad

It is very common, to see cables containing units of stranded pairs with a large number of pairs. There are also cables stranded in layers with paper-insulated star quads. Where the metric system is not in use, conductors of 0.41, 0.51 and 0.63 mm diameter (after conversion) are also possible, in addition to the 0.4, 0.6 and 0.8 mm types. The wires are usually designed as hollow, open insulated, wires without any paper "string"; less often are *paper pulp wires*. But solid and cellular PE insulated wires are frequently used.

It would take too long to detail all the different designs and the multiplicity of electrical properties that may be required. One special characteristic of the techniques used in USA is, however, of general interest here. When *splicing* or connecting together the separate lengths of manufactured cable during installation work in Germany, after the cable has been laid, the wires are connected together flush and smooth. This means that the pilot marker in each layer of one cable is connected to the corresponding marker in the other cable and so on continuously with the remaining strands without any changeovers. In the USA however, the splicing is sometimes arbitrary. This means that the pairs in each strand in the one cable are connected, in any order, to similar pairs in the other cable. When taking all the sections into consideration this is an advantage insofar as it produces an accidental, indirect, change in the twist of each of the consecutively-connected pairs.

But one must also accept the necessity of testing all the lines, from the beginning to the end of each section, to be able to connect them in their correct sequence onto the distributor in the exchange. Moreover, when there is intervention on the line it is not immediately possible to recognise the "sequential number" of each pair. This method is never used with polythene-insulated cables stranded in units. With such cables, the connections are made, as they are in Germany, in numerical sequence.

PE-insulated communications cables for private customers and special authorities

In this sphere outdoor cables having polythene-insulated conductors and a PE-sheathing are mainly used now.

These plastic cables contain generally St III star quads with copper conductors, either 0.6 mm or 0.8 mm diameter. On longer sections, such as pipe-line cables or long-distance cables for remote municipal water supplies, the cables usually have star quads with copper conductors 0.9 mm, 1.2 mm or even 1.4 mm diameter. Such cables are often *coil-loaded*, or are operated at *carrier frequencies* (Z12 system) and can, therefore, also be thought of as long-distance communication cables.

Because these lines, between subscribers, are directly-operated and require no conversion for a selector dialling system, their range is limited first of all by their loop resistance. There is the additional fact that such communications cables plants generally do not receive the same amount of maintenance and are not gas pressure supervised as is usual with the DBP. The result of all this has been that the standard insulation of the conductors with cellular PE, adopted (when the technique first started) to ensure low line-attenuation, has been rejected in favour of solid PE-insulation which, under the circumstances considered, improves operational reliability and because the lower line-attenuation in such circumstances is not absolutely necessary.

Polythene cables, where conductors have solid PE-insulation, have the further advantage that, unlike paper-insulated cables, they will still operate even if moisture has penetrated into the cable core. This is especially advantageous for the vital connecting cables of industrial supply companies such as, for example, the electric power companies, the water supply companies, as well as for pipe-lines. The local repair of the cable can consequently be undertaken at a time more suitable to the particular company.

To facilitate accurate measurement of any "wet patch" caused by external damage to the cable, a perforated pair of wires has been included in these PE cables. One side of the solid PE-insulation on the conductors of this wire is interrupted (at intervals of 60 mm). This perforated pair of conductors takes the place of a normally-insulated pair. In specially-designed cables it is usually provided as an extra feature in the cable core. If an insulation-monitoring apparatus is connected to the perforated pair it will automatically check the condition of the insulation in the cable, and, as soon as a specified insulation-resistance has been reached, will indicate that moisture has penetrated into the cable core. This value is higher than that at which any leakage attenuation on the other wires would have a disruptive effect. Where the cable connections are simpler, a frequently used telephone set can also be connected to the perforated pair of wires instead of the special apparatus. If there is moisture in the cable this particular telephone connection will of course fail earlier than the other wires, and the location of the fault can then be measured. To prevent water which has penetrated into one cable passing into the next length of cable, via the junction box, the *PE-welding sleeves* have threaded *plugs* inserted in each end.

To confine any water that has penetrated the cable core (as a result of damage) to the shortest possible length of cable, plugs are fitted to the cable core during manufacture. Such *cables with discontinuous fillers* contain, at intervals of approximately 20 m, an additional expandable substance which fills all the gaps in the cable core. If water should gain access its penetration, beyond the filler is prevented for a period of up to some three months. The length of the plug is between 0.5 and 1 meter.

For extensive use *continuously-filled* PE *cables* with conductors insulated with solid PE and a laminated PE sheath, such that no water can penetrate the cable core if the cable sheath is damaged, are available. At present, such cables are being produced with conductors 0.6 and 0.8 mm diameter and containing as many as 300 pairs. Cables stranded in layers are also made with 1.4 mm diameter conductors, but the number of pairs is then less.

Single-sheathed cables, which have an aluminium tape between the PE-foil wrapping on the cable core and the external PE sheath (for cable cores up to 17 mm this tape is flat; for larger diameter cable cores it is grooved), are only used for simple connections such as, for example, between buildings on private property. Such cables (A-2Y(St)2Y) have copper conductors 0.6 and 0.8 mm diameter, and are only produced by stranding them in layers. No continuous or discrete filling is provided, but they do have a perforated pair of wires.

Double-sheathed cables have a copper tape between the internal PE-sheath, which acts as a seal for the core wrapping, and the external PE sheath (for cores up to 17 mm diameter, this tape is flat; for greater diameters it is grooved). Because of their higher electrical strength between the wires and screen, they can also be used where there is an average amount of lightning, and where it is not much more practical to install cables specially protected against lightning.

These double-sheathed cables (A-2Y(K)2Y) are also produced with conductors of 0.6 and 0.8 mm, and have recently been stranded in units.

The same designs of PE cables can be used for laying in the earth or for conduit cable. Cables liable to considerable mechanical stresses during the laying process, or during operation, are provided with appropriate armouring which, with the exception of lightning-protected cable, is then covered with a protective coating of PE. Instead of the protective PE coating, armoured PE cable for oil pipe-lines has an oil-resistant protective covering of PVC. Cables used in underground-railway tunnels must also be provided with an external protective covering of PVC.

Details regarding the electrical properties of cables with copper conductors 0.6 and 0.8 mm diameter and concerning the marking of the wires and strands, are exactly the same as those quoted on pages 44 to 48.

2.5.3. Long-distance telephone cables (main district cables)

For intermediate-level networks which, being intermediate to the local and long-range networks, mainly provide the connections between the terminal exchanges and the central exchanges or between the terminal exchanges and the main exchanges, the DBP uses longer-range cables. Comparable to these longer-range cables are the telephone cables used for the sections of the German Federal Railways (DB). VDE 08 16 describes such cables as telephone cables for longer distances.

Generally, main district cables and *railway telecommunication cables* make use of paper-insulated strands mostly operated at low-frequencies. Hence the DBP use DM quads with conductor diameters of 0.8, 0.9 and 1.2 mm. The DBP also uses screened radio-broadcasting pairs (PiMF, i.e., pairs in metal foil) with conductors 1.4 mm diameter, and CF star quads with conductors 1.2 mm and 1.4 mm diameter, for the operation of CF systems Z12, V24, V60. Coaxial pairs 1.2/4.4 mm are also used.

Besides star quads with conductor diameters of 0.9, 1.2 and 1.4 mm utilizing phantom circuits (F-quads), the German Federal Railways also uses CF star quads with conductors 1.2 and 1.4 mm diameter, and small diameter coaxial pairs 1.2/4.4 mm impervious to the lateral penetration of water, to operate the V300 system.

All symmetrical paper-insulated strands are constructed with paper-string-insulated wires.

In most instances, quads operated at low-frequencies are coil-loaded.

The cables used abroad for main district operation are, basically, similar to the German designs. Because of their different system of measurement however the conductor diameters are p.e. 0.91, 1.02 and 1.27 mm.

The most-common component is the paper-string insulated wire, although, occasionally, solid PE-insulated wires are used.

VDE 0816 specifies the *method of marking and enumerating* the wires on symmetrical cables, stranded in layers.

The natural-coloured paper tape on the wires of every quad has coloured, longitudinal, stripes 2 to 3 mm wide. These are coloured as follows:

DM-quads, star quads St and *star quads St I* for the DBP;

Side circuit 1:	a-wire,	yellow
	b-wire,	red
Side circuit 2:	a-wire,	green
	b-wire,	blue

Star quads F for the German Federal Railways (DB);

> With 1, 3, 5 etc. quads per layer
> Side circuit 1: a- and b-wires, yellow
> Side circuit 2: a- and b-wires, red
>
> With 2, 4, 6 etc. quads per layer
> Side circuit 1: a- and b-wires, green
> Side circuit 2: a- and b-wires, blue

CF star quads for DBP and DB as for DM quads (see above);

Radio broadcasting pairs for DBP;

> a-wire, yellow or green
> b-wire, red or blue.

When the paper tape is spun onto the conductors, the longitudinal coloured stripes on the finished wires appear like coloured spirals.

Every stranded quad has a *quad spiral spun* around it, and this is usually of a natural-colour.

However, when it serves as the pilot marker of each layer, this spiral is coloured red.

The quad spiral for the directional marker in each layer is coloured green. If the directional marker "turns" clockwise with respect to the pilot marker, then the end of the cable nearest to the eye is the start end.

The *electrical properties* of main district and railway communications cables are specified in the special specifications of the DBP and DB. For quads operated at low frequencies, they are identical in principle to the corresponding requirement of VDE 0816 for long-distance telephone cables.

The specifications for the electrical values of screened radio-broadcasting pairs, CF quads and small diameter coaxial pairs are modelled on the recommendations of the CCITT. The values used in Germany are, generally, somewhat stricter.

The maximum permissible *operating* (peak) *voltage* for symmetrically stranded units in Germany is 225 V r.m.s. With reference to coaxial pairs, it is of interest that the intermediate repeaters are remotely fed with d.c., via the internal conductor.

The test voltages between wires, and between wire and sheath, are 500 and 2000 V r.m.s. – as they are for subscriber cables. The insulation-resistance is 10,000 M$\Omega \cdot$ km, and the loop resistance is dependant on the diameter of the conductors. All the other electrical values for symmetrically stranded elements are, usually, lower and have closer tolerances than is permitted for the components in subscriber cables. The reason for this is that main district and railway communications cables are media for long-range transmission, which makes much greater demands on electrical uniformity.

For DM-quads, St I, St and F quads, a nominal value for the *mutual capacity* is also specified and must be observed as accurately as possible. The individual and mean deviations from this rated value also have very close tolerances. In the instance of St III quads for subscriber cables, however, a maximum value of mutual capacity is all that is given. The deviations of the individual values can have any value; it is merely the maximum value which may not be exceeded.

To enable VF quads to satisfy the values for cross-talk required by international traffic it is essential, for main district cables, to have fairly low $k_{1,9...12}$ and $e_{1,2}$ couplings. Values for the $k_{2...8}$ and e_3 couplings are also specified for DM, St and F quads which use phantom circuit. In main district cables, maximum values for the *operational leakage* are specified for VF quads.

The line attenuation of VF quads on long-distance (main district) cables is much more satisfactory than that of St III quads used for subscriber cables. The reason for this is that long-distance cables generally have a lower loop resistance, and always have a lower mutual capacity.

When using CF quads the differences in resistance are usually even smaller than they are for VF quads which use phantom circuits. Since the *characteristic impedance*, in Germany, is given tolerances, it is sufficient to give the maximum value for the mutual capacity without mentioning tolerances. This is covered in the CCITT recommendations according to which either the scatter of the mutual capacitances, or the scatter of the characteristic impedance, determines the uniformity of the cable factory lengths. Insofar as paper-insulated CF quads can be used up to frequencies of 252 kHz (V60 system), and since the effect of the line-inductance has to be taken into consideration at these frequencies, it is more practical, and more justifiable, to give tolerances to the characteristic impedance. For CF quads, a maximum value is specified for the loss factor, tan δ since, in this instance, and in contrast with VF quads, the leakage attenuation becomes perceptible. With CF quads the capacitive couplings are considerably lower than with VF quads. At a frequency of 800 Hz, due to the mutual capacitance (which is lower than that of AF quads) the line-loss of CF quads is correspondingly lower.

Screened radio-broadcasting pairs are used for low-frequency transmission of audio broadcasting programmes up to a frequency of 15 kHz. Due to the screening there are no capacitive couplings between the broadcasting pairs and the other strands. Maximum values for the magnetic couplings, however, must not be exceeded.

The main district and railway communication cables are manufactured with a metal sheath. Depending on the method of laying, and the use to which the cable is put, protective coverings and, if necessary an armouring can be arranged around the sheath.

More modern main district cables in the DBP are supervised by gas pressure. This facility has not yet, however, been provided for the communication cables of the DB.

2.5.4. Long-distance (trunk) cables

The *long-distance trunk network* uses lines mainly employing CF four-wire systems. This network, is used for the connections in the upper network between the *main exchanges*, and the *central exchanges* and *main repeater stations* by which the regional network is connected to the international telephone network. The *long-range network* in the DBP includes the trunk level and main-district level networks. The electrical properties, which have to be guaranted for *long-distance cables*, and the necessarily exceptionally-high uniformity of the strands make essential, besides the highest standards of design and development, particularly high requirements for accuracy in manufacture.

The trunk cables used abroad may contain trunk lines, main district lines, and subscriber lines. Thus, the trunk cable supplied and installed in the Argentine, for example, by Siemens during the period 1954–63 had the following components.

The core-centre contained seven paper-insulated CF star quads with conductors 0.9 mm diameter, intended for Z12 systems at main district level; six standard (2.6/9.5) coaxial pairs used for long-distance V960 and television systems, for the trunk level; six PVC-insulated, 0.9 mm diameter signal wires, imbedded within the internal interstices of the coaxial pairs for the gas pressure supervising of the cable; three paper insulated VF quads, and three screened broadcasting pairs, all with 0.9 mm diameter conductors arranged alternating in the external interstices of the coaxial pairs. Although the screened pairs were provided for low-frequency transmission of radio broadcast programmes, up to frequencies of 15 kHz at the main district level, the VF quads were used partially for connections on the subscriber network and partially for connections in the main district network. A portion of CF channels is operated with an a.c. telegraphic system.

In other cases the long-distance cables supplied by Siemens to other countries have contained p.e. two, standard, coaxial pairs (2.6/9.5) and eight VF quads, or four VF and four CF quads (insulated with cellular-PE), or else four standard coaxial pairs and five VF/CF quads. Long-distance cables have also been supplied recently with a combination of small diameter coaxial pairs (1.2/4.4) and VF/CF quads.

In contrast, the long-distance cables of the DBP are used predominantly at the trunk level no matter whether they are coil-loaded, VF amplified, DM long-distance cables of the old type, or styroflex-insulated symmetrical CF long-distance cables, or coaxial CF trunk cables.

In addition to the technical advantages which modern CF trunk cables ensure as regards transmission characteristics, their main advantage is economic.

If the initial costs for an audio circuit are 100% per kilometre cable length, when using DM lines under VF operation, then, when using standard coaxial cables with CF operation (V960 system), they are only 7%. In both instances the portion due to the intermediate repeaters has been taken into consideration. This immense reduction in costs is due to the multiple use of the CF lines, and will be even more favourable when the V2700 four-wire system is used with standard coaxial pairs 2.6/9.5. The reduction in cost is also partly due to the considerable saving in copper. In the example quoted, for each 1000 km length of the audio circuit, only 0.28 tons of copper (instead of 15.2 tons) were required when operating with CF coaxial cable.

The DBP uses the following symbols for long-distance cables[1]:

Fk   for trunk line cables in the older VF network, the old broad-band cables, and coil-loaded CF cables with short loading sections

TFFk   for the new CF trunk cables, with symmetrical and coaxial CF lines

KxFk   for coaxial trunk cables, with several coaxial pairs

TFVk   for CF connection cables, to connect the broadcasting stations with repeater stations

OFk   for local trunk lines

AtFk resp. TF-AtFk or Kx-AtFk   for trunk distributing cables.

All the trunk cables in the DBP are known as *form cables*. Numerals in the abbreviated cable description indicate the number of pairs, one coaxial pair also being counted as a pair.

Lower-case letters after the number of pairs distinguish cables of different construction, which have the same number of pairs (for example with different stranding elements). A following number and, where necessary, the suffix letter indicate the sheath and the armouring as shown below:

1   unarmoured conduit cable having a lead sheath

1W   unarmoured conduit cable having a corrugated steel sheath and a plastics protective-covering

1L   unarmoured conduit cable having a smooth, aluminium, sheath and a plastics protective covering

2   armoured conduit cable having a lead sheath and a bedding

2L   armoured conduit cable having a smooth, aluminium sheath and a bedding

3   cable for laying in the ground, having a lead sheath, a bedding, armouring, and a serving of jute

3W   cable for laying in the ground, having a corrugated-steel sheath, a bedding, armouring, and a serving of jute

3L   cable for laying in the ground, having a smooth, aluminium sheath, a bedding, armouring, and a serving of jute

---

[1]) In 1976 the DBP will alter the symbols for long-distance cables in accordance with the type codes listed on pages 195–207.

4	river cable
5	bridge cable
10	cable for laying in the ground, having an improved reduction factor
11	conduit cable having an improved reduction factor

For example, the complete description for TFFk Form 14d1L is: a symmetrical CF trunk cable, with 14 styroflex-insulated pairs made as unarmoured conduit-cable with a smooth aluminium sheath and a plastics protective-covering.

Forms 14d and 17a are currently the best-known TFFk cables in the DBP. The cables are never laid with less than two tracks (one cable for each audio direction) and sometimes, there are four tracks, in the form of a huge figure eight, with many cross-connections and branches, from the north (via the west) to the south of Germany.

Form 14d and forms 4c and 8k are designed of star quads insulated with styroflex (string wires). The 17a cable has, at its centre, a standard coaxial pair for the V960, or, eventually, the V2700 system, and has a further eight star quads around insulated with styroflex. In every instance the star quads are for operation with the V120 system.

The four cable forms mentioned have four 0.5 mm diameter paper-insulated *testing conductors*, two of the wires being enamelled (Tietgen wires), contained within the cable core wrapping. These test conductors are required for insulation measurements and for the gas pressure supervision of the cables.

The coaxial pair 2.6/9.5 at the centre of the 17a TFFk cable is not screened with steel tapes if the intermediate repeaters are fed from a remote a.c. supply, but are, instead, screened with copper tapes. This prevents a *hum-modulation* of the signal potential transmitted on the symmetrical lines. Of course, the values for the far-end cross-talk between the coaxial pair and the star quads are not quite so satisfactory.

The first coaxial long-distance cable used by the DBP has four standard coaxial pairs 2.6/9.5 and five paper-insulated St I star quads, arranged at the centre of the cable and in the four external interstices of the coaxial pairs. The cable designation is KxFk Form 14f.

The more-recent long-distance cables used by the DBP are the 24f and 32c cables. The first-mentioned has twelve small diameter coaxial pairs 1.2/4.4 mm, six paper-insulated pairs with conductors 0.9 mm, and six solid-PE-insulated pairs with 0.6 mm diameter conductors. The 32c cable, in its initial layer (centre), has four standard coaxial pairs 2.6/9.5 mm; in the second layer there are eight standard coaxial pairs 2.6/9.5 mm, two units each of which contains four paper-insulated 0.9 mm diameter star quads, and four paper-insulated 0.9 mm pairs in four outer interstices.

The pairs and star quads in coaxial cables of the type KxFk are used for signal and testing purposes such as, for example, for the usual gas pressure supervisory system, for insulation measurements and as service circuits.

When using the standard coaxial pairs with the V10800 system a total of 64,800 channels in the audio-frequency band 0.3 to 3.4 kHz are available with a singly-laid form 32c cable.

3. Protecting communications cables against corrosion

If a communications system is dependent on cable connections, any damage to the cable sheath will certainly interfere with its operation and, in the majority of such incidents, will partially or totally interrupt all operation. This is especially true of communications cables where the conductors have paper- or styroflex-hollow-insulation, since they can no longer operate when penetrated by water or moisture through damage to the sheathing. Provided that the conductors are not broken, and that their insulation suffers no mechanical damage, communications cables with solid PE insulation are, operationally, much more reliable in the event of damage to the sheath. The operational reliability of cable installations is even more improved by using cables with pressurised gas or continuously-filled cables. Besides the loss of reception due to damage to the public communications cable network, and the sometimes costly disturbances in the operation of private and public undertakings, the removal of cable damage is also time-consuming and costly.

The damage done to communications cables is, principally, mechanical damage due to third parties through, for example, inadequate or complete lack of co-operation on local building sites, during constructional field work, for instance, or when laying pipe-lines or power cables in the vicinity of a communications cable run. Where a cable network is laid in conduit, damage to cables is, however, also caused by maintenance staff itself near cable manholes and through inexpert laying of the cables.

Sometimes the operation of communications cables, however, is also affected by the *corrosion* of the metal sheathing and/or any armouring that may be used. This frequently happens where metals, which generally do not have sufficient resistance to corrosion, are not provided (as they certainly should be) either with protective coverings or some electrical method of protection.

Corrosion implies the destruction of metal by *chemical* or *electro-chemical* and *electrolytic* action.

The process of metal decomposition, in which the anode (+) and cathode (−) regions are so close together that the currents produced cannot be detected with the usual measuring equipment is also sporadicly referred to as chemical corrosion. When a metal contact with an electrolyte, *local* electrochemical *cells* are formed as a result of variations in the composition of the metal or in its environment. The corrosion so produced should, however, be also considered as electro-chemical.

Electrolytic corrosion is an electro-chemical decomposition of a metal where measurable currents flow between the anode and cathode regions which are spatially separated. In this process the origin of the current is immaterial. It may be a matter of stray currents from electrical installations, or of currents produced by the varying reaction of the metal to different parts of the environment which make contact with it *(geological cells* or *macro-cells)*.

Electrons, i.e., negative-charge carriers, drift from the locality where there is an excess of electrons ($-$) to the locality where there is a lack of electrons ($+$). In practice, however, the direction of the current is assumed to be from positive to negative.

In the presence of an electrolyte the metal is deposited on the cathode ($-$). Consequently, by the electrical method of protection, the metal to be preserved is raised to a potential which is negative with respect to its environment, so that it prevents the removal of any metal by water or moisture in the ground.

3.1. Chemical corrosion

Because the anions contained in the electrolyte make contact with, for example, the lead sheath, the first stage of chemical corrosion is the production of salts at the anode surfaces, e.g., lead nitrate or lead sulphate, whilst alkaline materials are simultaneously formed at the cathode surfaces. As a result of the lead salts mixing with the alkaline substances, the second stage is the production of base salts which, being insoluble or very difficult to dissolve, can retard the process of corrosion on the lead sheath. In most instances the protective layer of salts so formed is insufficient, since it gets loosened by mechanical processes (expansions) and by the infiltration of water into the cable conduits and into the earth.

The corrosive effect of water is generally increased by nitrates and nitrites but is hindered by carbonates, sulphates, and silicones. When water flows over concrete or cement mortars, it releases alkaline substances (mainly chalk) which have a serious effect on lead, for example.

The basic white-lead to be found during the corrosion of lead is produced by the action of small traces of organic acids dissolved in the water. These acids are produced by the continuous disintegration of organic materials for instance such as oak and also jute.

Substances containing carbolic acid can also corrode lead sheathing. Consequently, any materials intended for the protective coverings of cables must be free of carbolic acid.

The processes by which metals in the earth become corroded are extremely complicated. In this respect the composition of the soil is of far greater importance than the composition of the metals. Moreover, the physical properties exert a greater influence than the purley chemical or biochemical properties.

Metals can be corroded by inorganic processes, initiated by some biogenetic stimulus, or by purely biogenetic processes.

Corrosion, when it is due partially or wholly to biogenetic stimuli, is caused by bacteria in the soil. Some types of soil bacteria initiate corrosion by increasing the carbon-dioxide content of the soil, or by producing sulphur from the hydrogen-sulphide content. Other bacteria cause the discharge of the oxygen in water. On a surface of iron or steel this causes the formation of bicarbonate or iron and, finally, iron hydroxide (rust).

The decomposition of organic materials in the ground, whether flora or fauna, is mainly due to soil bacteria. The products of this decomposition are, principally water and carbonic acid gas (carbon dioxide) but there are also very small quantities of sulphur, nitrogen, phosphorous etc. In this respect it is mainly the carbon-dioxide which has the corrosive effect in underground water. This can readily be detected by the fact that the corrosion products on a lead sheath largely, or even entirely, consist of carbonates.

Clay, and moorland soils, provide particularly suitable conditions for sulphur bacteria. They reproduce the sulphur contained in the hydrogen sulphide. The corrosion product from lead is then lead-sulphide which is, however, converted into lead carbonate by the action of hydrogen dioxide.

The aeration of the soil also has a considerable effect on corrosion. The renewal of the air in the neighbouring parts of the soil causes the formation of corrosion products.

Ground having low electrical resistance (i.e., with high electrical conductivity) favours corrosion due to the high concentration of ions in it.

As regards the content of salts in the ground, it should be noted that these dissolve the more readily as the temperature increases. The danger of corrosion is reduced in the presence of highly concentrated solutions of salts, since there is a restriction in the amount of air admitted.

Apart from chalky soil, the most dangerous types of soil are those containing humus. In addition to humic acid and inorganic salts, humus contains a high content of carbon dioxide which is continuously being replenished by bacterial action. In marshy and peaty soils the peaty acids are active. Polluted ground, containing industrial effluents and waste products which are not normally present in the ground, is often very aggressive. Such impurities may produce corrosion products by attacking metal directly, or may be the cause of the intense aeration (cinders, mining residues etc.).

Moisture, or water, is one of the most important factors as regards corrosion. Consequently, there is no danger of corrosion if there is no moisture content in the neighbourhood of the metal.

The pH value of the underground water or the soil is an important factor in the processes governing the corrosion of metal in the ground. According to definition, the pH value of a solution is the common logarithm of its hydrogen-ion activity a_{H+} multiplied by (-1). For very weak solutions this can also be replaced by the concentration of hydrogen-ions c_{H+} (in gram equivalents/litre):

$$pH = -\log_{10} c_{H+}.$$

The pH value ranges between zero $(1 \cdot c_{H+})$ and 14 $(10^{-14} \cdot c_{H+})$.

The pH value 7 is characteristic of a neutral solution. In the range 7 to 0 the solutions, as the concentration increases, become acid; they tend to alkalinity as the concentration increases in the range 7 to 14. Because the pH value of a fluid varies with temperature, the temperatures prevailing at the time of measurement must be supplied in addition to the pH value.

Irons and steels do not generally corrode in fluids with a pH value greater than 9.5. Lead and aluminium being amphoreric elements, react to both bases and salts. The surfaces of these metals are therefore attacked by stronger alkaline solutions.

Chemical corrosion can generally be detected by the composition and type of the corrosion products, and by the nature of its action. On lead, the principle items to be detected are lead-carbonate, lead-peroxide and also nitrites. The corrosion is uniform and, usually is only superficial. The holes produced in lead are not usually tunnel-like, but adept a somewhat deep, saucer, shape.

Metal sheaths, and armouring not intended to be electrically earthed, are protected against corrosion by various types of protective coverings – usually determined by economic factors. Bare lead-sheathed cables should not be laid directly in the ground. They are usually used as conduit cable. In districts where there is great risk of corrosion, even conduit cables have a protective covering generally consisting of a layer of some compound covered with a plastic sheath (PE) (passive protection against corrosion).

3.2. Electrolytic corrosion

The *electrolytic corrosion* which occurs in the presence of an electrolyte, is mainly due to stray currents. For lead, iron or steel, no corrosion is caused by alternating currents, provided that only these currents are present and that they do not experience any rectification. The cause of electrolytic corrosion is thus mainly direct current. Coming, for example, from tramway or railway installations with a partial earth return for the direct current, from d.c. power-supply networks with faulty insulation, or from very large rectifier plants, this direct current will affect the metal sheathing and/or the armouring. Since direct current installations are generally very extensive, they produce potential differences in various parts of the ground. Consequently, if communications cables must be installed in such an area, the metal sheath (and any armouring that may be present) will act as a conductor through which stray d.c. currents will flow by reason of the potential drop. In relation to its surroundings, the current will enter at the cathodes $(-)$ and leave at the anodes $(+)$.

Electrolytic corrosion usually only occurs at those points (anodes) and the metal from which the current flows into the surrounding ground. This is particularly true of iron and steel and, generally also, for lead. Corrosion of lead at the points (cathodes) where the current enters has, so far, only been detected on rare occasions. The assumed reason for this is the presence of large quantities of common salt or calcium in the electrolytes. Corrosion of lead at the cathodes is due to the amphoteric of lead oxides, which react equally to acids and bases. Unprotected aluminium is corroded both by alternating current and by direct current, of both polarities $(+$ or $-)$.

A type of corrosion which is not caused by externally produced e.m. f's and is, therefore, not caused by stray currents, must also be considered as electrolytic corrosion, if the flow of current can be determined with the usual measuring instruments. When metals are in contact with electrolytes, they can form electric cells.

In some sections, communications cables sometimes have metal sheaths made of different alloys or they are laid in ground whose composition varies. This causes small differences in potential which, generally, produce weak direct currents in the region between the metal sheath and the earth. On such rare occasions of electrolytic-corrosion, the anode regions are generally far distant from the cathode regions.

Electrolytic corrosion on lead etc. can be recognised by its effects. Deep furrows in the metal, and holes with steep walls or of tunnel form can be detected. Mostly, also, the crystalline structure is seriously affected. For lead, the corrosion products generally contain a large portion of sulphates. In severe instances lead peroxide is also present.

A corrosion current-density of 1 mA per dm^2 corresponds, on average, to a yearly disintegration of metal of some 0.12 mm (for iron and copper) some 0.15 mm (for zinc) and approximately 0.3 mm for lead.

Underground communications cables can be protected against electrolytic corrosion by several processes, which may have somewhat different effects. Several methods are often used simultaneously, to ensure the most effective protection.

Metals can be completely protected against corrosion if their surfaces are covered with some permanent insulation, impervious to water and moisture, with the result that any passage of current from or to the earth is obviated (passive protection). Mainly for economic reasons, however, this requirement usually cannot be achieved in practice.

Due to their relatively-large superficial area it would be too expensive to provide pipelines with such a permanent insulation covering. Moreover, it is impossible to guarantee that this protective covering will never be damaged during laying of the pipes. The insulation usually provided for pipe-lines does not usually give sufficient protection for the steel pipe. In most lengthy pipe-lines the possibility of electrolytic corrosion has to be taken into account. Thus, the inevitable, slight, impairments to the insulating cover are a particular source of danger to the steel pipe since, in the areas where the current flows out of the pipe, the small bare patches cause an increase in current density, and so intensify the electrolytic corrosion. Consequently, pipe-lines are generally protected against corrosion by a cathodic process.

Where there exists a great risk of corrosion, the simple protective coverings usually provided for communications cables are not sufficient without some layer which is impervious to water or moisture since the solidity of the protective covering usually deteriorates with increasing age. The metal sheathing and, where provided, any armouring, sooner or later reaches the earth potential of its environment, i.e., the cable becomes earthed. In contrast, plastic protective coverings and, in particular, polythene coverings with some compound as an underlayer, provide excellent protection against corrosion.

The metal sheaths and armouring of communications cables laid parallel to cath-odically-protected pipelines must be connected to the pipe-line cathode protection system, as, otherwise, the current which protects the pipeline would, arbitrarily, pass into and out of the metal sheaths of the cables and thus corrode them. The metal sheaths of communications cables behave as anodes which disintegrate rela-tively quickly. With cathode protection for communications cables, the armouring and the metal sheath are electrically connected. On the other hand, the metal screen of a plastics-insulated communicating cable is insulated from the armouring. Where pipe-line cables have plastic-insulated conductors and plastics sheathing, both below and above the armouring, the cathode protection equipment is much less expensive than in the instance of earthed-cable arrangements, which require much heavier protective currents and which therefore regularly increase the operating costs.

Pipes provided with cathode protection are frequently electrically-insulated at specified intervals by incorporating insulating sleeves or pieces of pipe which are not electrical conductors such as, for instance, concrete pipes in long-distance water supplies. The result of this is to restrict the excessive propagation of stray currents along the pipe-line and to reduce the expense of the protective equipment. The insulating units should be laid in ground which is dry all the year round, or which has a high ground-resistance i.e., a low conductivity. In districts where there is danger from lightning, the insulating sleeves or pipes must be bridged with anti-sparking devices.

The ohmic resistance of the metal sheath and armouring of a communications cable is higher, by some powers of ten, than that of the steel pipe-lines of average and large diameter. Generally, therefore, it is not necessary to provide any electrical insulation with insulating sleeves for the metal sheaths of communications cables connected to the pipe-line cathode protection system.

The purpose of insulating sleeves in communications cables is, generally, to ensure that sections of the network are mutually independent i.e., to interrupt any electrical connection of the cable sheaths and armourings in the network. In addition to providing sufficient and permanent insulation, the insulating sleeves must also possess a mechanical resistance and solidity. Where several cables run together in parallel, the insulating sleeves must be fitted to each cable and in the same position. Normally the metal sheaths of all cables which run parallel to one another are electrically connected together in front and at the back of the insulating sleeves.

At points where communications cables and pipelines meet, carrying stray currents and not, it is advisable to insulate the cables or pipes from each other. If any one of the pipelines or cables has cathode protection, all the other related installations must also share this protective system. Consequently, all the metal parts (sheaths, armouring, pipes) must be electrically connected together.

When planning a communicating cable installation precautions must be taken to ensure that the cables are laid as far as possible from any d.c.-operated plant such as d.c. railways or large rectifying installations, so as to restrict or prevent the "trespass" of stray currents into the metal sheathing of the cables. The number of points at which the cable actually crosses the conducting rail of a d.c. railway, or suddenly reduces its distance from it, must be reduced to a minimum, since this produces an increase in the exchange of currents between the rail and the cable. Any electrical connection between the metal sheathing of the communication cables and the railways, or the conducting jointed parts should be prevented or the metal sheathing must be included in an electrical protection system.

In areas where d.c. installations may endanger the cabling, satisfactory protection has been obtained by enclosing the cables in iron or steel pipes. The protecting piping must of course have proper electrical connections, at both ends, to any cable armouring that may be provided.

To limit and/or reduce the stray currents produced by d.c. railway systems, efforts must be made to prevent the passage of these currents to earth by ensuring that the railway current return-line (whether a rail or special return conductor) is properly insulated with respect to earth. Further, the return of this current where it occurs, for example, via rails, must be facilitated by making the electrical resistance of the rail as small and as uniform as possible, with the help of connectors across the rails joints.

3.3. Electrical protection

The metal coverings (sheath, armouring) of ground-laid communications cables and other subterranean metallic conductors can be protected against electrolytic corrosion by electrical methods of protection which involve maintaining all the metal surfaces at a potential which is electrically negative with respect to their electrolytic environment (e.g., underground water, effluent, or moist earth) i.e., transforming these surfaces into cathodes. In addition, a direct-currents field must be created within the electrolytic environment, which will enter the metals (cathodes) at every point at which they make direct contact with the electrolyte; this will flow along these metals, (the cable sheath for example), and will again be returned to the environment (anode) at predetermined points. The d.c. current opposed to the corrosion current must, therefore, not merely compensate for the corrosion current, but must ensure (and this is of even greater importance) that this current also has access to all of the metal surfaces in need of protection, so as to reduce their potential to such an extent that no more metallic ions can be released. This method of cathode protection is also known as *active protection against corrosion*.

Relative to a copper/copper sulphate electrode ($Cu/CuSO_4$) the value of the protective voltage for lead is generally -0.55 V$_-$ and for iron or steel -0.85 V$_-$.

At the points where the current leaves the metal sheaths requiring protection, connections must be made to quantities of metal properly insulated with respect to their environment, and which are either connected to the protective anodes (electric cells) embedded in the ground, or to the metals (e.g., the iron rails) which behave like anodes and which consequently, provide the disintegrated metal.

On principle, it is possible to protect iron, steel, copper, lead etc. from corrosion, by electrical methods. In the instance of aluminium and its alloys however, this is not possible since this material becomes corroded by both anode and cathode electrodes.

By improving the insulation which covers the metal requiring protection and by reducing its line resistance, the necessary protective currents are reduced. This is also a means of avoiding undesirable repercussions on extraneous installations in the neighbourhood.

Whatever type of protective method is selected the methods discussed must be applied, not merely at those points where corrosion is detected, but must cover the complete installation and any neighbouring installations. Continuous supervision of the protective equipment and, on occasion, of the installations requiring protection, is unavoidable.

3.3.1. Protective procedures on d.c. railways

When providing protection against stray currents from d.c. railways, an effort is always made to derive the protective current from the railway installation *(electrical drainage)*. If necessary, currents from a separate d.c. source can be superimposed.

When utilizing *direct electrical drainage* the metal protective coverings of the communications cable are connected, via insulated metal-conductors, directly to the rails, to a return conductor, or to the negative bus-bars of the railway supply. This method, however, can only be used provided that the direction of the current never changes under all the conditions under which the railway supply network is operated. Brief transient, reversals of low amperage can be excepted. It is, however, essential to ensure that at the points selected the rails concerned are always electrically-negative with respect to earth.

Much greater safety is provided by *polarised* (directional) *electrical drainage*. In this method, devices such as rectifiers or switches with polarised tripping relays are connected to the insulated connections between the rails and the installations to be protected. By this method the currents can only flow in one direction.

Where the stray currents are exhausted *(enforced electrical drainage)* the metal coverings of the cables to be protected are connected via insulated leads to the negative $(-)$ pole of a source of direct current, from which the positive pole $(+)$ is connected to the rails. The effect of this method is intermediate between the methods of polarised drainage and cathode protection. In this instance the rails form the anode.

3.3.2. Cathodic protection

When using *cathode protection*, with an anode buried in the ground, the metal requiring protection – such for example, as the metal sheathing and armouring of a communications cable, or the steel pipe in a pipeline – is connected by a properly-insulated metallic conductor (e.g., at least $4\,mm^2$ of copper), with the negative $(-)$ pole of a d.c. source. The positive $(+)$ pole from this same source is connected via an identical conductor to a mass of metal (usually a piece of iron rail) buried in the ground (usually in finely-grained coke), to provide a good connection to earth. This mass of metal acts as the anode, but anodes of graphic and iron silicide are also common. To increase its effective range of action, the anode must be located at a sufficient distance from the equipment to be protected. This distance generally amounts to some 10 to 100 mm. Precautions must, however, be taken to ensure that there are no components present to obstruct the flow of the protective current between the anode and the metals requiring protection. The pieces of rail usually disintegrate within three to five years.

Pipelines are divided into sections approximately 10 km long, by the incorporation of insulating sleeves or pieces of non-conducting piping. By reason of the relatively high line-resistance, this division is usually unnecessary for communications cables. The protective currents are supplied to the equipment requiring protection at specified intervals. In the instance of the pipe-line sections mentioned above, these supplies are provided at the beginning, middle, and end of the sections, since this produces an extensive and uniform distribution of the protective potential. If the requirements are not however, satisfied, the potential distribution can be made more uniform by means of additional feeder points or control equipment.

The magnitude of the protective current depends on the voltage of the source (usually a rectifier, fed from a local mains supply) and on the resistance of the circuit formed by the ground, the anode buried in it, the connecting leads and the equipment to be protected. It must be taken into account that the anode resistance rises slowly, as a result of the corrosion products which form on its surface.

It is, consequently, necessary to inspect the anodes at regular intervals and to renew them in good time if their resistance, which should normally only be a few ohms, becomes excessive.

In practice, depending on the quality of the insulation, the current densities on the surfaces to be cathodically protected vary between $0.3 \, \text{mA/m}^2$ and $3 \, \text{mA/m}^2$. If the metals to be protected have no insulation however, the currents may be as high as $50 \, \text{mA/m}^2$. It is, therefore, advisable to provide communications cables with a protective covering which gives proper insulation, such as, for example, an external polythene sheath.

In simpler instances it is possible, instead of the d.c. sources mentioned, to use anodes made of a baser metal than the metal requiring protection, e.g., zinc, and magnesium or their alloys and which, in conjunction with the electrolyte, behave like electric cells. These anodes, which are thus simultaneously sources of current and material for disintegration, are in electrical conductive connection with the metal requiring protection. To ensure that they always provide this protective action they must, however, be inspected at very frequent intervals.

4. Calculating the lengths of communications cables for drawing them

Communications cables are drawn in cable duct plants (conduits), either by means of a *cable grip* (where the diameter of the cable beneath the sheath is less than 50 mm) or by a drawing ring applied to the cable in the cable factory (where the diameter of the cable beneath the sheath is greater than or equal to 50 mm or, in exceptional instances, when it is greater than 30 mm). Cables armoured with round and flat wire are generally drawn with the armouring formed into a loop.

Unarmoured cable

The cable grip transmits the tensile force almost entirely to the sheathing, and only to a very small extent to the cable core. In such instances, therefore, only the tensile loading strength of the cable sheathing has to be taken into consideration for any rough calculation of the possible *drawing length*. For plastic-insulated cables with double sheaths, e.g., A-2Y(K)2Y, the calculation can be based solely on the external sheath as the supporting element.

For cables equipped with drawing rings, however, the drawing length is calculated via the tensile loading capacity of the cable core, when corrected by the factor (130-D)/100. The correction factor is used because all the conductors are not subjected to the same tensile load if there are a large number of pairs.

Cable armoured with steel tape

Cable, armoured with steel tape, can only be drawn in conduits if the armouring is surrounded by an external protective covering of PE or PVC. The steel tape armouring must not be subjected to any tension. Consequently, when drawing cable with a cable grip, the steel tape armouring (and both the serving and bedding) must be cut back to let the cable grip seize onto the cable core. The cable grip is then pushed some 0.4 m over the serving to prevent any displacement of the protective coverings and armouring when the cable is drawn.

Formulae and examples

The following is the general formula for calculating the maximum permissible length of cable (l_{max} in km) that can be drawn:

$$l_{max} = \frac{A \cdot \sigma_{max\,perm}}{\eta \cdot G}$$

where A is the total cross-section of the cable element being loadad (sheath, core, armouring) in mm²

$\sigma_{\text{max perm}}$ is the maximum permissible tensile stress in $\dfrac{\text{daN}}{\text{mm}^2}$

η is the coefficient of sliding friction

G is the net weight of the cable in $\dfrac{\text{daN}}{\text{km}}$

The cross section that can be loaded, A (in mm²), is calculated as follows:

For conductors

$$A_{\text{conductor}} = (\text{Number of conductors})\ \frac{(d)^2 \cdot \pi}{4} \cdot \frac{(130 - D)}{100}$$

For smooth cable sheaths

$$A_{\text{sheath}} = (D + s) \cdot \pi \cdot s;$$

where d is the diameter of a conductor in mm

D is the diameter beneath the sheath in mm

s is the nominal wall thickness of the sheath in mm

π circle figure (approx. 3.14).

For armouring

$$A_{\text{armour (round or flat wire)}} =$$
$$= (\text{Number of wires in armouring}) (\text{Cross section of one wire})$$

The values for the specific tensile stress ($\sigma_{\text{max perm}}$) are:

for soft copper	$\leqq$	5 daN/mm²
for pure lead	$\leqq$	0.8 daN/mm²
for lead alloy	$\leqq$	1.1 daN/mm²
for aluminium	$\leqq$	3.6 daN/mm²
for flat and round wire	$\leqq$	13.5 daN/mm²
for PE and PVC	$\leqq$	0.5 daN/mm².

The product ($A \cdot \sigma_{\text{max perm}}$) in the general formula indicates the maximum permissible tensile force F_{max} (in daN) that can be used to draw the cable.

The following are values for the coefficient of sliding friction, η:

where the route is unknown	1.0
for cables laid in cast-concrete cable conduits without bitumen and with minimum displacements approx.	0.9
for cables in clean conduits coated with bitumen or in glazed tubings	0.9 to 0.7

for PE cables in hard PVC or hard PE pipes   0.5 to 0.3

for cables drawn over cable rollers suitably closely arranged   0.3 to 0.2.

Calculated examples

(a) Calculate the maximum permissible length of plastic cable type A-2Y(K)2Y
500 × 2 × 0.8 St III that can be drawn, if the cable, which is provided with a
drawing ring, has 500 pairs with conductors 0.8 mm diameter, has a net weight
of approximately 7525 kg/km, and is to drawn through clean bitumen-lined
conduits. The calculation is made as follows.

The cross section that can be loaded is

$$A_{conductor} = 500 \cdot 2 \, \frac{0.8^2 \, \pi}{4} \cdot \frac{(130 - 60)}{100} \approx 350 \, mm^2 \, .$$

The maximum permissible tensile force is

$$F_{max} = 350 \cdot 5 = 1750 \, daN \, .$$

The maximum permissible length that can be drawn becomes

$$l_{max} = \frac{1750}{0.9 \cdot 7525} \approx 0.26 \, km = 260 \, m;$$

in this case the more unfavourable value for the coefficient of sliding friction
has been used.

(b) Calculate the maximum permissible length that can be drawn for a plastic cable
type A-2Y(K)2Y 100 × 2 × 0.8 St III Bd which has a hundred pairs 0.8 mm
diameter, is stranded in units, has a net weight of approximately 1715 kg/km
and is to be drawn with a cable grip in a hard PVC pipe. The calculation is
performed as follows.

The cross-section that can be loaded is

$$A_{sheath} = (30.6 + 2.2) \cdot \pi \cdot 2.2 \approx 227 \, mm^2$$

and the maximum permissible tensile force is

$$F_{max} = 227 \cdot 0.5 \approx 113 \, daN \, .$$

The maximum permissible length that can be drawn therefore becomes

$$l_{max} = \frac{113}{0.5 \cdot 1715} \approx 0.13 = 130 \, m \, .$$

5. Illustrations of communications cables

The planet we inhabit is surrounded with a compact communications network. Inter-continental telephone conversations, teleprinter installations and the exchange of data are now commonplace, but the vast amount of effort spent by engineers in the development of communications cables is much less-known because the transmission routes, when they take the form of cabling, are usually in the earth or on the bed of the sea.

This chapter supports the presentation of communications cable technology by illustrations. Some illustrations here reveal the complex construction and close tolerances of the manufacturing techniques required to produce communications cables for high-quality transmission. Samples from the wide range of cables supplied by Siemens reflect the importance of this branch of engineering, which has developped since the invention of the gutta-percha press in the mid-19th century by Werner von Siemens, to the development of the modern coaxial cable in use today.

Section through the core of a plastic-insulated cable for local subscriber networks.
The different strands are marked with insulation of different colours

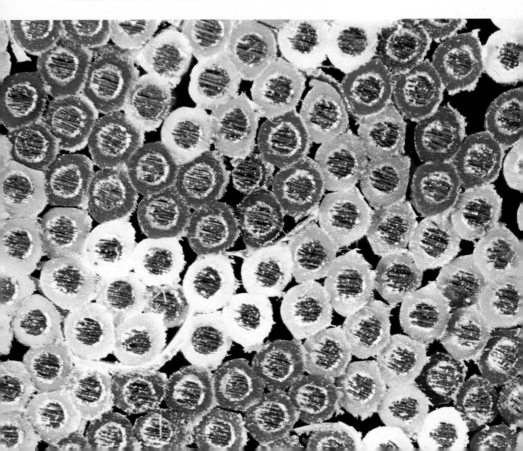

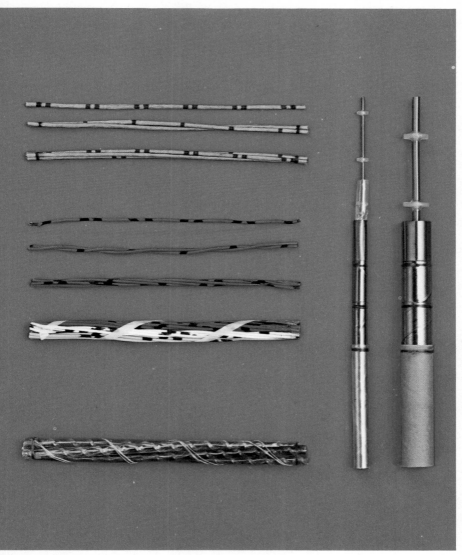

A small selection from the broad
range of communications cables

Cable components
Paper-insulated
wire
pair
quad

PE-insulated
wire
pair
quad
basic unit

Styroflex-insulated
quad

Coaxial pairs
1.2/4.4
2.6/9.5

73

The strands are stranded into a
cable-core on a special machine.
Above: Stranding a paper-insulated
cable in layers
Right: Stranding a plastic-insulated
cable in units

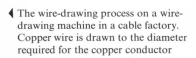 The wire-drawing process on a wire-
drawing machine in a cable factory.
Copper wire is drawn to the diameter
required for the copper conductor

Seamless application
of the plastic sheath
to the cable core

Armouring a communications cable
with two steel tapes as an additional
protection against compressive stresses
and inductive interference

Siemens communications cables go all over the world. Loading cable drums in India

A coaxial cable being laid in the Argentinian pampas, in a cable trench excavated by a ditcher

In suitable ground, communications cables can be ploughed in by a single mechanical process

78

Jointing PE communications
cables with PE electrical
welding sleeves

Screw-clamping sleeves facilitate ▶
the assembly of filled
communications cables

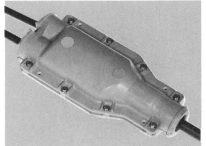

Remotely supplied wide-band ▶
repeaters are housed in
pressure tight underground
containers

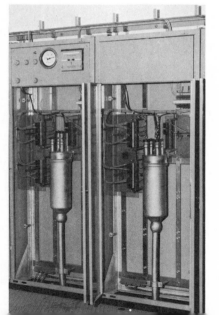

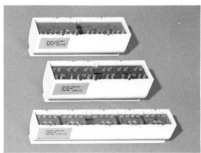

Loading coils increase the range of
V.F. lines

▲
Gas pressure supervised long distance
coaxial cables are connected together
with pressure tight sleeves

◀ Gas pressure supervised long distance cables
terminate in pressure tight distributing
sleeves

Communications cables – Telephony

switchboard
cable
PVC-insulated

Filled external PE cable, stranded in units

Conductor
dia. 0.4 mm

Conductor
dia. 0.8 mm

Unit type cable with
a double sheath

Communications cables – Telex

Paper-insulated external cable, stranded in layers

External cable stranded in units with a laminated sheath

Armoured

Unarmoured

Solid PE-insulation

Cellular PE-insulation

Communications cables – Television

Long distance cable	Long distance cable	Long distance cable	HF Cable
symmetrical styroflex-insulated	with 12 small diameter coaxial pairs	with 6 small diameter coaxial pairs and 8 standard coaxial pairs	21/61 Cu2Y

Communications cables – Railway signals engineering system

Signal cable armoured	Railway station communications cable	Railway communications cable	Railway communications cable A combination of symmetrical strands and 2 small diameter coaxial pairs
Solid PE-insulated	Cellular PE-insulated	with symmetrical strands	

Communications cables – data transmission

Installation cable
for SIMATIC installations

Self-supporting aerial cable
simultaneously overhead earth wire

Long distance cable
for pipe-line installations

System cable
for metropolitan and underground railways with corrugated-aluminium shea

6. Transmission engineering

The task of electrical communications engineering is the problem of producing a communications system which will provide economic and reliable transmission of information with the greatest possible accuracy even over great distance.

Electrical telecommunications systems consist basically of a *transmitter*, a *transmission route*, and a *receiver*. Where the transmission route consists of wires, the cable is of particular significance.

This section discusses the essential electrical properties of cables in a basically simple manner.

The frequency range required for the transmission of information, via cabling, ranges from 0 to approximately $11 \cdot 10^9$ Hz (11 GHz), as shown in Table 2.

It is obvious that it is impossible to operate with a single type of cable over a frequency range which is so wide and so fully used. In the region up to approximately 550 kHz *cables with symmetrical conductors* have become of great importance. The attainable range of such a system of conductors depends not so much on its *operational range* (loop impedance) as on the *line attenuation* which increases with rising frequency. *Coaxial lines* are used in the frequency range 60 kHz to 6 GHz.

Because cables must be operated practically without any form of interference or faults, very exact methods of manufacture are essential. Cable design depends on calculations reinforced, to some extent, by experimentally-obtained values.

The electrical processes involved in the transmission of information along symmetrical and coaxial cables can be understood with the help of transmission-line theory.

Type of transmission	Frequency range
D.C. Telegraphy	up to 60 Hz
A.C. Telegraphy	up to 3.2 kHz
V.F. Telephony	0.3 to 3.4 kHz
Sound broadcasting	up to 15 kHz
Television broadcasting	approx. 5 MHz
Carrier frequency transmission	up to 60 MHz
H.F. Transmission	up to 11 GHz

Table 2
Frequency ranges
for transmission
of information

6.1. Transmission-line theory

The *transmission equations* are generally derived from an equivalent circuit (Fig. 19).

Each line has an *ohmic resistance R*, an *inductance L*, a *leakage G*, and a *capacitance C*. For a theoretical analysis it is assumed that the quantities R, L, G and C are uniformly distributed over the whole length of the conductor, i.e., they are proportional to the length of the conductor.

A line is described as *homogeneous* if, throughout its whole length the conductor, the insulation, and the stranding of the cable are of the same quality. This means that, inter alia, the material of the conductor, its cross-section, the distance separating the conductors from each other and from the screen (e.g., sheathing), the operating temperature, the moisture content, the dielectric constant and the thickness of the insulation are the same at all points on the line. Slight deviations, which are inevitable in practice, are taken account of in the specifications.

The four *line constants*, also known as *constants of proportionality*, are in practice related to a cable 1 km long.

These line constants are also known as:

$$\text{Distributed resistance } R' \text{ in } \frac{\text{ohms}}{\text{km}}$$

$$\text{Distributed inductance } L' \text{ in } \frac{\text{H}}{\text{km}}$$

$$\text{Distributed leakage } G' \text{ in } \frac{\text{S}}{\text{km}}$$

$$\text{Distributed capacitance } C' \text{ in } \frac{\text{F}}{\text{km}}$$

In practice, the usual values are $\dfrac{\text{ohms}}{\text{km}}$, $\dfrac{\text{mH}}{\text{km}}$, $\dfrac{\mu\text{S}}{\text{km}}$ and $\dfrac{\text{nF}}{\text{km}}$.

It is known that electro-magnetic energy is propagated along a conductor in the form of a wave. To analyse the properties of a conductor mathematically, any mixture of frequencies (total oscillation) at the input to a conductor is resolved into its partial oscillations. Analyses can thus be performed for all the frequencies in the respective range.

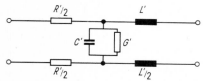

Fig. 19   Equivalent circuit for a homogeneous line

Further, in any mathematical analysis, one starts with an element of length x, at a distance Δx from the beginning of the cable, and considers it sufficient if the equations for the propagation of purely sinusoidal waveforms can be derived. This is obviously permissible since, according to FOURIER, any non-sinusoidal process can be resolved into a sum of sine waves. Ideally, therefore, each separate oscillation in the spectrum of sine waves travels along the cable, at the end of which the partial oscillations are recombined.

The partial calculation for these processes is expressed in the form of differential equations, the solutions for which give inter alia, the value of

$$\gamma = \pm \sqrt{(R' + j\omega L')(G' + j\omega C')}\,.$$

The quantity, γ, which is the *propagation constant* of the cable, is dependent on the frequency

$$\omega = 2\pi f$$

and on the four line-constants. Here f, the theoretically fundamental frequency, is measured in units of $1/s$, and π is the measure of a circle in radians (approximate value 3.14).

The propagation constant γ is a complex number which can therefore be written in the form:

$$\gamma = \pm (\alpha + j\beta)$$

where the real part α, measured in Np/km, is called the attenuation constant and the imaginary (j-)part, β, measured in rad/km, is called the phase constant (wavelength constant).

These constant quantities α, β, and γ are measured relative to a unit length of cable, the practical unit being a cable length of 1 km.

When these quantities are related to actual lengths of cabling, then the term *unit* is used.

The complex *propagation unit* is

$$g = \gamma \cdot l = (\alpha + j\beta)\, l \text{ or } a + jb\,.$$

The *attenuation unit* is

$$a = \alpha \cdot l$$

and the *phase* or *wavelength unit*, in radians, is

$$b = \beta \cdot l$$

where l is the length of the cable in km.

The *amplitude* of the wave is attenuated, i.e. it decreases, along the cable in proportion to the attenuation unit *a*.

The *phase unit* is an expression of the fact that, in addition to its attenuation, the voltage vector, e.g., of the wave voltage, experiences a phase-shift which is dependent on the length of the cable.

The propagation of the oscillations along the cable can be described in the following way.

A small rod (vector) assumes the $0°$ position at the beginning of the cable. The length of this rod indicates the amplitude of the oscillation. As the rod now moves along one axis of the cable is gradually shortened, by a specific amount, until it reaches the end of a wavelength and it simultaneously revolves about the axis, through $360°$, as it makes this advance. If such a rotating model is observed from the side, then an upper and lower curve-envelope can be distinguished which represent the attenuation of the amplitude. When observed in the axial direction, the end of the rod furthest from the axis travels through $360°$ during one cycle and, by its continuous contraction, as it travels along the conductor, produces a gradually-contracting helical envelope.

The *wavelength* of a conductor is calculated from the ratio

$$\lambda = \frac{2\pi}{\beta} \; ; \text{ where } \lambda \text{ is the wavelength in km.}$$

The *phase velocity*, expressed in km/s, is

$$v_p = \frac{\omega}{\beta}$$

and is the velocity at which a (sine-)wave of frequency *f* will travel along the conductor.

The reciprocal of the phase velocity, called the *phase delay time*, is

$$\tau_p = \frac{1}{v_p} = \frac{\beta}{\omega}$$

and is expressed in s/km.

This is the time within which a wave travels along a conductor 1 km in length.

A communications signal, however, is composed from a spectrum of frequencies in which the individual oscillations are continuously varying with respect to time. To be able to transmit a message without distortion, all the frequencies in the spectrum (the frequency band) must have the same propagation time. In this instance the propagation time of the group of frequencies (group propagation time, τ_g) and the separate frequencies (phase delay time τ_p) are of corresponding magnitude.

$$\tau_g = \tau_p = \frac{\beta}{\omega}$$

τ_g, the *group propagation time* is expressed in s/km.

In actual practice the frequency characteristics of the quantities τ_p and τ_g deviate within specified limits from this ideal situation. Some limitation of this deviation can be achieved by the use of appropriate devices connected to the telephone equipment.

For telephone connections the CCITT[1] has specified maximum values for the various (group) propagation times within a frequency band. Compared with a minimum (group) propagation time, the maximum deviations in this time (maximum (group) propagation time distortions) may amount to 30 to 60 ms, in the upper and lower limiting frequency in any transcontinental connection.

If the propagation time is more than 300 ms, then disturbances can occur in the flow of conversation or complete interruption of the conversation. CCITT has also specified typical (group) propagation times (14 ms to a maximum of 50 ms) which are valid for 12 series-connected channel-end-pairs between the limiting frequencies (300 Hz to 3400 Hz). There is a direct connection between the differences in the propagation time at the limiting frequencies and the *syllable intelligibility*.[2]

The effect of a difference in propagation time of 100 ms ($\hat{=}$ 60% syllable intelligibility) is that the diphthong 'iu' spoken into the cable input is heard as 'ui' at the output, because the lower frequencies are transmitted faster then the higher frequencies.

In addition, to its deterioration with differences in propagation time, syllable intelligibility is also dependent on attenuation. If the audio (speech) frequency-band is limited to between 300 and 2400 Hz, and the attenuation between two subscribers is 0 the syllable intelligibility that can be attained at the receiving station (in the earphone) is only 70%. If the attenuation is 31 dB (3.6 Np) or 36 dB (4.2 Np) then the syllable intelligibility is reduced respectively to only 60%, or some 55%. Within the audio frequency band of 300 to 3400 Hz, as recommended by the CCITT and generally in use today, the intelligibility values are a little better, i.e., higher.

Besides syllable intelligibility there is also the notion of *sentence intelligibility*. There is a relationship between the two. A syllable intelligibility of 70% corresponds, on average, to almost 100% sentence intelligibility, when using plain language. A syllable intelligibility of 70% is thus a criterion for a "highly intelligible" trans-

---

[1] International Advisory Committee for Telegraphy and Telephony

[2] According to CCIF "intelligibility" is the ratio of the number of correctly-understood portions of a conversation (e.g., sounds, syllables, logatomes, words) to the total number of similar portions in the conversation.

mission of information. A noticeable deterioration in intelligibility occurs as soon as the syllable intelligibility is reduced to between 50% and 40%. If the syllable intelligibility only amounts to 20% to 25% then, due to the need for repetitions, twice as much time is needed to transmit the message. In a high-quality telecommunications system (e.g., audio and video film broadcasting up to 15 kHz, with negligible band width limitation) the syllable intelligibility is approximately 98%. Intelligibility is spoilt by ambient noise and parasitic noise on the lines.

Another term which, in addition to the transmission constant γ also defines a cable, is obtained from the solution of the above differential equations. This term is the *characteristic impedance* measured in ohms, which has the properties of a complex resistance,

$$Z_{\mathrm{L}} = \sqrt{\frac{R' + j\omega L'}{G' + j\omega C'}}$$

where $R' + j\omega L'$ is the distributed impedance
and $G' + j\omega C'$ is the distributed admittance.

The complex characteristic impedance Z_{L} can also be represented as

$$Z_{\mathrm{L}} = Z_{\mathrm{r}} + jZ_{\mathrm{i}}$$

where Z_{r} is the real part of the characteristic impedance, and Z_{i} is the imaginary part.

The characteristic impedance Z_{L} defines the ratio wave voltages to the wave currents at every point along the conductor. Assuming uniform quality of manufacture, it is therefore a quantity which is independent of place and time. It is also a criterion for the *matching* of the line i.e., if a cable is exactly terminated by its characteristic impedance, or, if the line connected to it has the same characteristic impedance, then the oscillation (wave) arriving at the end of the first line is not reflected.

On the other hand the transmission constant γ defines the attenuation and the velocity of the wave along the conductor.

The first mentioned formula for the transmission constant γ can be resolved into

$$\alpha = \sqrt{\frac{1}{2}(G'R' - \omega^2 L'C') + \frac{1}{2}\sqrt{(R'^2 + \omega^2 L'^2)(G'^2 + \omega^2 C'^2)}}$$

and

$$\beta = \sqrt{\frac{1}{2}(\omega^2 L'C' - G'R') + \frac{1}{2}\sqrt{(R'^2 + \omega^2 L'^2)(G'^2 + \omega^2 C'^2)}}.$$

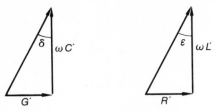

Fig. 20   Admittance and impedance triangles

The exact equation for the attenuation constant is in the wellknown form

$$\alpha = \frac{R}{2Z_r} + \frac{G \cdot |Z_L|^2}{2Z_r}$$

In all cases of small phase angle of Z_L (i.e., $Z_r \approx |Z_L|$), the following approximation can be derived from the previous equation.

$$\alpha \approx \frac{R}{2 \cdot |Z_L|} + \frac{G \cdot |Z_L|}{2} \ or \approx \frac{R}{2Z_r} + \frac{G \cdot Z_r}{2}.$$

The *loss angles* δ and ε are further terms from transmission theory. They are defined by means of the admittance and impedance triangles shown in fig. 20.

Here, $\tan \delta = \dfrac{G'}{\omega C'}$, is the leakage-current loss factor, whilst $\tan \varepsilon = \dfrac{R'}{\omega \cdot L'}$ is the line resistance loss factor.

6.1.1. Line constants in a symmetrical line

The attenuation, propagation time, and characteristic impedance of a line are dependent, as mentioned in 6.1, on the four line-constants R, C, G and L and on the frequency. Some of the constants are also affected by the temperature. It will therefore be advisable to examine the properties of the four line-constants a little more closely. Since the line constants, in practice, are on principal related to a length of 1 km, in the rest of the discussion the characteristic prime ' (e.g., R') will be omitted, since it only indicates that one is dealing with values which are related to length. Values based on any other lengths can be converted to 1 km.

Loop resistance R and small differences in resistance ΔR

It is obvious from the statements in 6.1. that, if for example, the attenuation is reduced then the resistance R of the line loop is also reduced. The loop resistance R is dependent on the material properties of the conductor and on the condition under which the line is operated.

93

R increases

- as the specific resistance ϱ of the conductor material increases
- as the cross-section q of the conductor increases
- as the operating frequency f (skin effect) increases, and
- as the temperature t increases.

If both conductors of a line are made of the same material and have the same cross-section then the d.c. resistance of a symmetrical line is

$$R = 2 \cdot \frac{\varrho}{q}$$

where R is the d.c. resistance in ohms related to a length of 1 m; ϱ is the specific resistance of the conductor material in ohms $\cdot$ mm^2/m; and q is the cross-section of the conductor in mm^2.

In practice, when the resistance R is given, it is stated in relation to a length of 1 km, so that the values calculated by means of the above formulae must be multiplied by 10^3.

The loop resistance R can be reduced either by increasing the cross-section of the conductor, or by using conductor material of lower specific resistance. To increase the cross-section, however, is not economical because, for any given number of pairs in a cable, the cable core diameter increases and a greater quantity of sheathing material is required. The increased weight and thickness of the cable would create difficulties when winding it onto the drum, as would transporting and, finally, laying the cable (ducts).

The material used for the conductors, consequently, has a lowest possible specific resistance, so as to reduce its cross-section. Moreover, the cost of materials has to be taken into consideration.

For telecommunications cables, copper is preferred to aluminium. Due to the higher specific resistance of aluminium, cables made of this material, when they have the same electrical properties and the same number of pairs as copper cables, are some 25% thicker. Copper, however, also has better mechanical properties.

The specific resistance of electrolytically-deposited copper wire (soft-annealed) for telecommunications cabling at a temperature of 20 °C should not exceed

$$\varrho_{20} = 0.01754 \ \frac{\text{ohms} \cdot \text{mm}^2}{\text{m}} .$$

The reciprocal of the specific resistance, the electrical conductance, $\varkappa$, must in this instance be at least

$$\varkappa_{20} = 57 \ \frac{\text{S} \cdot \text{m}}{\text{mm}^2} .$$

To make the single wires fit properly into the stranding units, and to ensure that these fit properly into the cable core, soft-annealed wire is generally used for the conductors of telecommunications cabling (on the other hand, the internal conductor on a 2.6/9.5 coaxial pair is semi-hard).

With quads hard copper would cause excessive couplings within the quad.

The purity of aluminium for telecommunications cables must be at least 99.5%. In its soft-annealed state, at a temperature of 20°C, the specific resistance of aluminium must be not less than

$$\varrho_{20} = 0.02778 \; \frac{\text{ohms} \cdot \text{mm}^2}{\text{m}}$$

or, its conductance must be at least

$$\varkappa_{20} = 36 \; \frac{\text{S} \cdot \text{m}}{\text{mm}^2} .$$

Since the wires are stranded in pairs, or in quads, and since these are stranded into the cable core, loop resistance of a cable line must be correspondingly greater than the value that would be obtained from the previously-mentioned formula relative to a conductor 1 km long, because the length of the conductors, due to the stranding, is greater than the length of the cabling. In specifications giving the values for the loop resistance, this fact is already allowed for by the stranding factor. The stranding factor is calculated from the mean value of the line length of all kinds of stranding and numbers of pairs of a specified conductor relative to 1 km length of cable.

With any increase in frequency the resistance of a conductor, or the line resistance, increases. In such instances the term *effective resistance* is used and the term d.c. resistance, which depends on the total cross-section of the conductor, is discarded. The reason for this is the phenomenon of current displacement, commonly known as the *skin effect*. The conductor's own magnetic field induces a current which is directly opposed to the operating current within the conductor. By reason of the skin effect the effective resistance (a.c. resistance) of a conductor at high frequencies is greater than d.c. resistance, because the operating current only flows along the outer skin of the conductor. Thus, as regards the operating current, the effective cross-section is lower, and its resistance higher, than that of a similar d.c. conductor. To express this in another way, the effective resistance of a conductor acts as though the current could only penetrate the conductor to a specified depth, although it is evenly distributed over this area. The following depths of penetration ϑ are obtained for copper.

Frequency	ϑ in μm
1 MHz	68
100 MHz	6.8
10 GHz	0.68

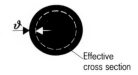

Effective cross section

The skin effect is of no importance in symmetrical VF telecommunications cabling. When calculating the line characteristics of coaxial pairs, or HF cables, however, this must be allowed for. Here, one can benefit by reducing the wall-thickness of the external conductor. In the HF region, considerable losses (increased attenuation) are caused by the skin effect. Generally, at frequencies above some 100 kHz, the

attenuation increases in the proportion $\sqrt{\dfrac{f}{f_0}}$.

The use of strands for HF cabling is also explained by the skin effect. Because the full cross-section of any single conductor is not used by the operating current, it is the custom to strand together thin wires with a radius smaller than the depth of penetration ϑ. These wires must be electrically isolated and are therefore covered with a thin insulating layer of lacquer.

Over a wide temperature range the specific resistance of pure metals increases linearly with temperature. The following equation gives the resistance

$$R_t = R_{t_0} \left[1 + (t - t_0)\right] ;$$

where R_t is the resistance at temperature t; R_{t_0} is the resistance at the ambient temperature (usually $+ 20°C$); α is the temperature coefficient of the conductor material e.g., for copper this is $3.9 \cdot 10^{-3}$ per $°C$ (usually the value $4 \cdot 10^{-3}$ per $°C$ is used) whilst for aluminium it is $4.0 \cdot 10^{-3}$ per $°C$; t is the instantaneous temperature of the item under measurement (e.g., the conductor); t_0 is the ambient temperature (usually $+ 20°C$).

When measuring, for example, any loop resistance, it is thus clear from the formula that, to be able to indicate the guaranteed value (for example, $+20°C$), it is also necessary to make a simultaneous test of the temperature of the measured object for the simple reason that a temperature deviation of, say $\pm 10°C$ from normal temperature, causes, in the instance of copper, a change of approximately 4% in its resistance.

For high-quality symmetrical lines, values for the *differences in resistance* must be also guaranteed in addition to the loop resistance R, and these values must not be exceeded.

The resistance differential within the side circuit of a quad is the difference between the line resistance of the a and b wires

$$\Delta R_{sc} = R_a - R_b .$$

The equation valid for the phantom circuit is

$$\Delta R_{quad} = \left(\frac{R_a \cdot R_b}{R_a + R_b}\right)_{sc\,1} - \left(\frac{R_a \cdot R_b}{R_a + R_b}\right)_{sc\,2} .$$

In general, the following approximation is applicable.

$$\Delta R_{\text{quad}} = \frac{1}{4} \left[(R_a + R_b)_{\text{sc } 1} - (R_a + R_b)_{\text{sc } 2} \right].$$

In high-quality symmetrical lines the resistance differentials must be small in order to obtain high values of cross-talk attenuation. Moreover, if the resistance differentials are too high, this can cause excessive voltage differences between the conductors or lines, under conditions where the lines can be affected by external influences (e.g., by main power supplies).

Mutual capacity C_B

The capacitance of a line is determined by the geometrical arrangement of the conductors in the cable core and by the type of insulating material between the conductors.

The capacitance of a line increases

- as the distance separating the conductors decreases
- as the surface of the conductors increases
- as the relative dielectric constant increases
- as the temperature increases (e.g., when the conductors are insulated with paper)
- as the temperature falls (when the conductors are insulated with PE i.e., polyethylene)
- as the humidity increases.

In the instance of cable lines it is not sufficient merely to consider the partial capacity between a pair of conductors in a line. The partial capacities between the conductor and any neighbouring conductors, for instance, between the other conductors and the cable sheath (screen), are of importance. The equivalent capacitance C', symbolically represented in Fig. 19, must be considered as the summation of many partial capacitances. As the total capacity of a line, this is defined by the well known term of mutual capacity, C_B, $\left(\dfrac{\text{nF}}{\text{km}} \right)$.

A simple example of the way to derive the mutual capacity of a screened pair is given in section 1.3.1.

The attenuation, and therefore the high quality of the line depends on the mutual capacity C_B. To produce a low mutual capacity, the distance separating the conductors in the line must be as large as possible (for economic reasons there are, obviously, limits to this distance) and the insulating material should have a dielectric constant, (DC) ε_r, as near as possible to that of air. After a vacuum, air has the lowest dielectric constant

$$\varepsilon_{r \text{ air}} = 1.000594 .$$

Material	ε_r at a frequency of 800 Hz, and a temperature of $+20\,^\circ$C
PVC	3 to 8
Paper	2.1 to 2.3
PE	2.1 to 2.3
Styroflex	2.4

Table 3
Relative dielectric constant of various materials for insulating the conductors in telecommunications cables

The materials mentioned in Table 3 are those principally used for insulating the conductors for telecommunications cables. They are easily worked, are economical, and have a sufficiently-high dielectric strength.

By reason of the proportion of air in the conductor insulating material (e.g., paper stringed wire) the resultant DC ε_r of the lines in the cable is, sometimes, considerably lower than the relative DC ε_r of the insulating material itself.

The distance between the conductors cannot be arbitrarily large because of the need to keep the cable cross-section as small as possible. Separating the two conductors in a line within a cable core as far as possible (e.g., to operate the conductors in various quads as a line) is impossible because of the high symmetry and uniformity of the lines necessary for crosstalk.

With paper insulation the mutual capacity is but little dependent on temperature, within the usual ranges. The temperature coefficient at a frequency of 800 Hz is only $+0.5\%_{00}$ per degree of change in temperature. The values for other insulating materials are similar.

In contrast, however, the mutual capacity very noticeably increases with any increase in moisture absorbed from the air by the insulating paper. Paper is hygroscopic, i.e., it absorbs moisture from the air. Consequently paper-insulated cables have to be dried during manufacture. Humidity very considerably increases the resulting DC of the insulating paper since the dielectric constant of water, ε_r, is approximately 80.

When water penetrates a cable, paper- and styroflex-insulated lines break down. On the other hand, where cables are completely polyethylene insulated (PE) also in cases of unfilled cables, they usually continue to operate. Of course, in such instances, the mutual capacity in the wetted portions increases by some 150% and the attenuation increases by some 60%. However, the attenuation over the whole connection is not usually so greatly increased by the "soaked" sections of the cable so as to exceed the permissible total attenuation and to interrupt operation. Cables of this sort can be repaired later, at a time to suit the customer.

Leakage current G; insulation resistance R_{is}

The leakage current G defines the effective portion of the shunt current between the two conductors in a line. This cross current may be caused by insufficient or faulty insulation (low insulation resistance) and also by "row-electrification action" in the insulating medium (dielectric losses). Properly dried, paper-insulated cables and cables insulated with synthetic materials have high insulation resistances (up to some tens of $G\Omega \cdot km$). Consequently the leakage losses are principally due to the dielectric losses, which are seriously affected by frequency.

At a frequency of 800 Hz the values for the leakage current G, which is also known as the operating leakage current, are of the order of magnitude

$$G = 10^{-6}\,S = 1\,\mu S\,.$$

At low frequencies the leakage current G is almost directly proportional to the frequency. As the frequency increases, the increase in the leakage current is more pronounced and is no longer linear. In practice, the preferable criterion for the leakage current, or the dielectric losses, is the loss factor

$$\tan \delta = \frac{G}{\omega \cdot C}\,,$$

which for dry, paper insulated cable at a frequency of 800 Hz is approximately $3 \cdot 10^{-3}$.

Because of the sudden increase in the leakage current at the higher frequencies, the fraction of the total attenuation attributable to leakage current attenuation correspondingly increases. Consequently, instead of using paper-insulated star quads, styroflex-insulated star quads are used for transmission systems where the bandwidth exceeds 250 kHz (V 120 system, up to 552 kHz). At the higher frequencies the loss factor, $\tan \delta$, of styroflex is lower than that of paper by approximately one order of magnitude ($\tan \delta \approx 2 \cdot 10^{-4}$).

The leakage current G and, consequently, the loss factor $\tan \delta$, are dependent on temperature. The leakage current has a negative temperature coefficient, i.e., the leakage current drops as the temperature rises.

The insulation resistance $R_{is} = \dfrac{1}{G_{tot}}$, measured under d.c. voltage conditions, and is the reciprocal of the sum of all the partial leakage currents

$$G_{tot} = G_1 + G_2 + \dots + G_n\,,$$

and can also be thought of as all the partial shunt resistances connected in parallel. The data are usually stated in $M\Omega \cdot km$ or $G\Omega \cdot km$.

For a specified length of cable the absolute insulation resistance, $R_{is\,abs}$, measured in megohms, is calculated to be $R_{is\,abs} = R_{is}/l$; where R_{is} is the insulation resistance of the cable in megohms $\cdot$ km (the guaranteed value) and where l is the length of the cable in km.

Example

$$R_{is\,abs} = \frac{10\,000}{5}\left(\frac{M\Omega \cdot km}{km}\right) = 2000\ M\Omega$$

With reference to leakage current and insulation resistance, paper-insulated cable has a temperature coefficient of -6% per degree of variation in temperature, i.e., as the temperature drops, the value of the insulation resistance drops and as the temperature rises, so the insulation resistance rises.

The following equation describes the insulation resistance

$$R_{is\,t} = R_{is\,t_0} \cdot \left[1 - \alpha(t - t_0)\right]$$

where $R_{is\,t}$ is the insulation resistance at temperature t; $R_{is\,t_0}$ is the insulation resistance at ambient temperature (usually $+20\,°C$); α is the temperature coefficient, e.g., $6 \cdot 10^{-2}$ for paper; t is the instantaneous temperature of the component under measurement (usually a wire relative to all the other wires and the screen or earth); t_0 is the ambient temperature (usually $+20\,°C$).

To be able to give a guaranteed value for, say, $+20\,°C$, it is thus obvious that the temperature of the component must be determined at the same time as its insulation resistance is being measured, since a change in temperature of $\pm 10\,°C$ will effect a change in resistance of 60%.

Because the insulation resistance, R_{is} is "in parallel" in cable installations, account must be taken of the fact that, during measurements of such installations, dirty or damp terminal fittings on the cable will give a total value for $R_{is\,abs}$ which is lower than the least of the partial resistances e.g., that of a dirty cable termination, even although the cable itself satisfies the specification. Consequently, before making end-to-end measurements, all the accessible cable terminations should be cleaned and dried.

If moisture has seeped through the cable core itself, the insulation resistance is also reduced; i.e., even a damp cable termination gives the impression that the whole cable is poor. If there is water in the cable, then those parts of the stranding which are solely insulated by air space become short-circuited. In contrast, the insulation resistance of those parts of the stranding completely insulated with PE (polyethylene) only falls very slowly, when water is present, to a value which is usually only two tenth powers below the value for dry cabling. Of course, for VF operation of PE-insulated telecommunications cables such a reduction in the insulation resistance is of no significance, since the fraction of the total attenuation attributable to leakage-current attenuation only makes itself noticable when the absolute insulation resistance $\leq 50\,k\Omega$. By using a pair of "perforated" wires, contained in the cable core and in which the insulation covering is perforated at specified intervals, the moist areas in any PE cable can, however, be promptly and inexpensively located.

When marking measurements it must be remembered that the value of the insulation resistance depends on the length of the time that the voltage has been applied. When measurement starts, the insulation-resistance value rises steeply and then slowly, and symtotically. To obtain accurate measurements, d.c. voltages between 100 V and 500 V must be applied for a period of at least one minute.

Inductance L

The *inductance* of a symmetrical line is the sum of its external and internal inductance

$$L = L_{ext} + L_{int} \,.$$

The external inductance L_{ext} is dependent on the magnetic field outside the conductor, and is therefore effectively determined by the ratio of the distance separating the conductors in the line to the conductor diameter. This quantity L_{ext} is largely independent on frequency.

The internal inductance L_{int} depends on the magnetic field within the conductor, i.e., at higher frequencies on the cross-section of the conductor. This quantity L_{int} is dependent on frequency and, as a result of the current displacement (skin effect) mentioned on page 95, it decreases when the frequency increases.

From a consideration of the partial inductances it is clear that the inductance of a symmetrical cable decreases with increasing frequency. In the audio frequency band (0.3 to 3.4 kHz) the value of the inductance is approximately 0.7 mH/km. Direct indication of this value must not be given for factory lengths.

The value $\omega \cdot L$, in the audio frequency band is low compared with the loop resistance. Thus, in this frequency band the transmission constant, γ, and the characteristic impedance, Z, are almost independant on the inductance L. In the higher frequency range, however, for example in the carrier-frequency range, the values γ and Z are substantially dependent on the inductance L.

6.1.2. Coil-loaded line

Both the attenuation constant and the characteristic impedance are dependent on frequency. Fig. 21 shows the graphs for these quantities expressed as functions of frequency for normal (i.e., not coil-loaded) lines operated at audio frequencies.

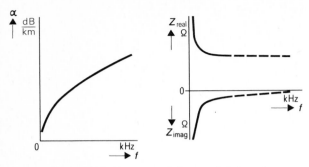

Fig. 21 Attenuation constants and characteristic impedance
as functions of frequency

Figure 21 shows that the line attenuation increases with increasing frequency, i.e., the individual frequencies in, for example, the speech-frequency band have different attenuation values. In long lines this causes *attenuation distortions* which spoil intelligibility.

The attenuation of VF lines that are not coil loaded rises relatively steeply in the speech frequency band (0.3 to 3.4 kHz). Consequently, such cables are not suitable for long distance.

As far back as 1890, Heaviside developed the idea of reducing the attenuation of symmetrical cable lines by artificially increasing their inductance with coils.

The following equation for the attenuation constant of a line is approximately true also in the low-frequency region

$$\alpha = \frac{R}{2}\sqrt{\frac{C}{L}} + \frac{G}{2}\sqrt{\frac{L}{C}} = \alpha_R + \alpha_G$$

where α_R is the resistance loss constant and α_G is the leakage current attenuation constant.

In cables, the *resistance loss* is thus the preponderant value, if the inductance L is increased by connecting coils to the circuit then the resistance loss is correspondingly reduced. Because both the resistance loss and the *leakage current loss* are dependent on the values of L and C, and since C is practically constant, the attenuation constant α can be reduced to a minimum by increasing the inductance L, to a specified value. This happens if the leakage current loss is of the same order of magnitude as the resistance loss. Expressed in another way, the attenuation constant of a conductor is a minimum if the ratio R/L is as small as the ratio G/C (the Heaviside ratio).

There are two well-known methods for the technical realisation of the Heaviside relationship; the continuous load method, sometimes called the Krarup method (named after its Danish inventor, 1902), and the coil-loading or Pupin method (M.J. Pupin developed in 1901 a practicably applicable system with coils).

By means of the continuous-load method, now largely only of historic interest, the increase in the inductance of the conductors was achieved by winding about them, over their whole length, a ferromagnetic material (iron wire) of some 0.2 to 0.3 mm thickness. Due to the uniformity that can be attained in the additional distributed inductance, this method was predominantly used for marine cables and for the intermediate or terminating cables of open wire transmission lines.

With the coil-loading method a higher inductance is attained by means of the coils. These coils are called *Pupin coils* after their inventor. Cables with artificially-increased inductance were of decisive importance in electrical transmission engineering, when it was still impossible to increase the range of a cable with amplifiers. The earliest repeater stations were only operated in 1920. It can also be said that transmission through cables, and over great distances, was first made possible by Pupin coils.

These Pupin coils consist of a shell-type core of magnetic material (silicon-ferrite coils) with two separate windings, respectively connected to the forward and return lines. The total magnetic flux is the sum of the fluxes produced in the two coils.

The pupin coils are connected at uniform intervals along the line. In Germany, the usual distance between coils, s (loading (coil) section), is 1.7 km whilst in other countries it is sometimes 1.83 km.

Because of the possibility of cross-talk, the Pupin coils are arranged, to reduce the coupling to a minimum, in loading-coil housings or sleeves (loading point).

Pupinisation (coil-loading)

Figure 22 shows the coil loaded side-circuit of a quad, and the associated equivalent circuit schematically.

Theoretically, a coil-loaded line can no longer be considered as a homogeneous line but must be treated as an artificial line consisting of low-pass filters. A loading section is therefore identical with a low-pass filter section.

As regards the construction of coil-loaded lines a distinction must be made between the European and American types. The European type (see Fig. 22) begins and ends with a half loading section ($s/2$). The advantage of this system is that the coils, for the whole connecting line, can be of standard value (e.g., 80 mH). The USA type begins and ends with coils of half the standard inductance ($L_{sp}/2$), hence in this type coils with half (e.g., 44 mH) and with the full standard inductance (e.g., 88 mH) are

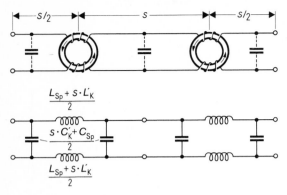

L_{sp} Coil inductance per loading section L_k Cable inductance per km

C_{sp} Coil capacitance per loading section C_k Cable capacitance per km

s Length of loading section

Fig. 22   Coil-loaded side circuit of a quad with its equivalent circuit

required. As regards the attenuation unit a, and the phase unit b, both types are identical. The characteristic impedance, however, has a different frequency characteristic as shown in fig. 23.

According to the theory a distinction is made between the *passband* and the *cut-off range suppression band*. For the given characteristic impedance the limiting frequency f_0 represents the boundary between the two.

A loaded line begins with $\frac{s}{2}$, it forms a recurrent network of low-pass filters in delta-connected circuit ($\triangle$) and with $\frac{L_{sp}}{2}$ it forms a T-section circuit.

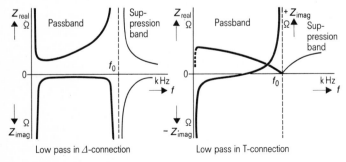

Fig. 23   Frequency characteristic for the characteristic impedance: left commencing with $\frac{s}{2}$; right commencing with $L_{sp}/2$

In the delta-connected circuit $\left(\text{commencing with } \frac{s}{2}\right)$ the imaginary part of the characteristic impedance always maintains its capacitative character. Within the pass-band it first drops to a minimum and then starts to rise once again. Here, the minimum covers practically the whole transmission range for an AF system.

For the T-section circuit $\left(\text{commencing with } \frac{L_{sp}}{2}\right)$ the imaginary part of the characteristic impedance, initially starting from infinity, is at first capacitative but gradually becomes inductive and then rises to infinity at the limiting frequency.

The punctual insertion of the inductance prevents the increase in the attenuation constant of a coil-loaded line from being proportional to frequency (as is the instance for a line without coils; see fig. 21) but adopts a sort of S-form as shown in fig. 24.

In the central portion of the transmission range the attenuation curve generally has a much smaller gradient, usually being practically horizontal. At the higher frequencies, particularly within the range of the cut-off frequency f_0 the attenuation increases very steeply. At the cut-off frequency it is some 2 to 10 times greater than in the transmission region. Above the cut-off frequency, transmission becomes impracticable; indeed, it is impossible.

When considering the frequency characteristic of the attenuation constant, it is understandable that within the pass-band it cannot follow any uniform law with respect to all the frequencies between $f = 0$ and f_0. At the lowest frequencies, for which the ratio $\frac{\omega \cdot L}{R} \leqq 0.1$, the coil inductance is still unnoticeable. The frequency characteristic for the attenuation constant thus corresponds in this region to an unloaded line, i.e., to a line without coils. In the next region, in which the wavelength is still large relative to the coil spacing, the coils have the effect of inductances uniformly-distributed along the line with the result that, in this region also, a coil-loaded line behaves like a homogeneous line without coils. In the actual transmission region the attenuation is very largely constant, i.e., it is only to a very small extent dependent on frequency. In the neighbourhood of the cut-off frequency however, its increase is greater than linear. Consequently, the approximation formula

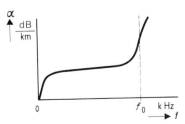

Fig. 24
Frequency characteristic for the characteristic impedance of a coil-loaded line

for the attenuation constant α of a loaded line normally only takes into consideration the frequency range that can be used for transmission.

A coil-loaded line, in comparison with a normal AF line not only has a lower attenuation, it is also distinguished by the fact that it has a much smaller attenuation distortion within the transmission band, and is therefore suitable for use over much longer lines (e.g., also with AF amplifiers).

Because the attenuation constant has a steep slope in the neighbourhood of the cut-off frequency, a coil loaded line can generally only be used up to approximately 70 to 80% of the cut-off frequency. One disadvantage of a coil loaded line is its longer propagation time, and the propagation time distortions within the transmission band.

For a low-pass (coil loaded) line the equation for the cut-off frequency is

$$\omega_0 = \frac{2}{\sqrt{L \cdot C}} \, ; \omega_0 = 2\pi \cdot f_0 \, ;$$

whence

$$f_0 = \frac{\omega_0}{2\pi} = \frac{1}{2\pi} \cdot \frac{2}{\sqrt{L \cdot C}} = \frac{1}{\pi \cdot \sqrt{L \cdot C}} \, .$$

The calculation of the cut-off frequency f_0 is usually made for a loading section of length s.

Thus

$$L = L_K + L_{sp} \quad \text{and} \quad C = C_K + C_{sp};$$
$$L_K = L'_K \cdot s \quad \text{and} \quad C_K = C'_K \cdot s;$$

where L_K, the distributed cable inductance is about 0.7 mH/km for main lines, and about 0.4 mH/km for phantom lines; s is the length of a loading section in km; L_{sp} is the coil inductance per loading section in mH; C'_K is the distributed cable capacitance in nF/km; C_{sp} is the coil capacitance per loading section, which is approximately 0.1 nF for single coils and the phantom circuit of loading coil units, resp. about 2 to 3 nF for the side-circuits of loading coil sets.

The cut-off frequency for a coil-loaded line is then calculated as follows

$$f_0 = \frac{1}{\pi \cdot \sqrt{(L'_K \cdot s + L_{sp}) \cdot (C'_K \cdot s + C_{sp})}}$$

or

$$f_0 = \frac{1}{\pi \cdot s \sqrt{\left(L'_K + \frac{L_{sp}}{s} \right) \cdot \left(C'_K + \frac{C_{sp}}{s} \right)}} \, .$$

Example

$$s = 1.83\,\text{km}\;;$$

$$L'_K = 0.7\,\frac{\text{mH}}{\text{km}}\;;\qquad L_{sp} = 66\,\text{mH}\;;$$

$$C'_K = 36.0\,\frac{\text{nF}}{\text{km}}\;;\qquad C_{sp} = 0.1\,\text{nF}\,.$$

Then

$$\frac{L_{sp}}{s} = \frac{66}{1.83} \approx 36.1\,\frac{\text{mH}}{\text{km}}\qquad\text{and}$$

$$\frac{C_{sp}}{s} = \frac{0.1}{1.83} \approx 0.054\,\frac{\text{nF}}{\text{km}}$$

$$f_0 = \frac{1}{\pi \cdot 1.83 \cdot \sqrt{(0.7 \cdot 10^{-3} + 36.1 \cdot 10^{-3}) \cdot (36.0 \cdot 10^{-9} + 0.054 \cdot 10^{-9})}}$$

$$\approx \frac{1}{\pi \cdot 1.83 \cdot \sqrt{36.8 \cdot 10^{-3} \cdot 36.054 \cdot 10^{-9}}} \approx \frac{10^6}{\pi \cdot 1.83 \cdot \sqrt{1326}}$$

$$\approx \frac{10^6}{\pi \cdot 1.83 \cdot 36.4} \approx 4780\,Hz\,.$$

Using an assumed limit for the useful frequency range $\frac{f_{\text{lim}}}{f_0} \leqq 0.75$, then, in this instance, the upper transmission frequency becomes:

$$f_{\text{lim}} \leqq 0.75 \cdot 4780 \leqq 3585\,\text{Hz}\,.$$

With St-, F- or DM-quads also the phantom circuits (see 1.3.2.) may be loaded besides their side-circuits. Fig. 25 illustrates the principle. In actual practice, however, the side circuit coils are sometimes split in the middle and the phantom coil is connected to these halves (symmetrical coil assembly).

Figure 25 makes it clear that the currents (magnetic fluxes) of the side circuits are neutralised in the phantom circuit, whilst the magnetic fluxes (currents) in the phantom coil are neutralised in the side circuit coils.

To ensure that the phantom coil will not cause cross-talk between the phantom circuit and the two side circuits, the inductance, effective resistance, and the partial capacitances of the four partial windings must be very accurately balanced with respect to the coil core and to earth.

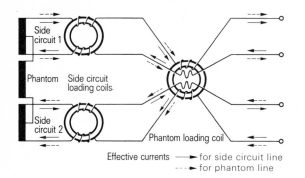

Fig. 25
Coil loading of a
phantom circuit at St-, F-
and DM-quads

Side circuit 1

Phantom   Side circuit
             loading coils.

Side circuit 2

Phantom loading coil

Effective currents ——► for side circuit line
                  ----► for phantom line

When designing a coil-loaded system the technical and economic aspects must be taken into consideration; for instance, determining the cut-off frequency and selecting the length of the loading sections (the spacing between the coils).

The cut-off frequency is a function of the length of the loading section, the inductance of the coil and the capacitance of the line.

If the possibility of reducing the mutual capacity is dispensed with, since it generally assumes expensive stranding units, the cut-off frequency then becomes dependent, substantially, on the inductance of the coils and the length of the loading section. The choice for the length of the loading section is principally determined by economic factors. The optimal coil spacing, at which the line attenuation becomes a minimum is usually very small. In addition to the large number of loading points over the whole line which than become necessary, this also causes of the unsatisfactory result that the leakage-current attenuation amounts to approximately half of the total attenuation. For practical reasons this is most undesirable since the leakage current is very seriously affected by temperature and moisture. In practice, therefore, the usual distance between coils is a larger than the optimal distance at any given frequency.

When determining the inductance of the coils, consideration must be given to the fact that, although the line attenuation is more rapidly reduced, the cut-off frequency and, consequently, the useful frequency bandwidth are reduced if the inductance values are too high. Conversely, if the coil inductances are reduced, although the cut-off frequency rises, there is also an increase in the line attenuation. For economic reasons standard coils are used instead of coils with individually-calculated inductances. These standard coils cause deviations from the theoretically-obtained optimum transmission properties. These deviations however, are technically permissible.

When loading phantom circuits with coils, it must be taken into consideration that the mutual capacity of the phantom circuit, when using star quads (and when using DM-quads) is greater than the appropriate side circuit capacity by factors of respectively 2.7 (and 1.6).

If the phantom and side circuits have the same cut-off frequency then the characteristic impedance Z_0 of the phantom circuit becomes for:

Multiple twin-quads: $\qquad Z_{0\,\text{Phantom}} \approx \dfrac{Z_{0\,\text{side circuit}}}{1.6}$

Star quads: $\qquad\qquad Z_{0\,\text{Phantom}} \approx \dfrac{Z_{0\,\text{side circuit}}}{2.7}.$

Further, since the effective resistance of the phantom circuit, due to the parallel connection of the two associated side circuit conductors, is only approximately half the effective resistance (i.e., approximately the loop resistance) of the side circuit, the attenuation constant in the phantom circuit becomes for:

Multiple twin-quads: $\qquad \alpha_{\text{Phantom}} \approx 0.8 \cdot \alpha_{\text{side circuit}}$

Star quads: $\qquad\qquad \alpha_{\text{Phantom}} \approx 1.35 \cdot \alpha_{\text{side circuit}}.$

The phantom circuit is, therefore, coil-loaded in such a way that it has the same attenuation as the side circuit. Then, with star quad phantoms, and with multiple twin-quad phantoms, the cut-off frequencies are respectively some 20% lower and some 20% higher than the cut-off frequency of the side circuit. The quality of the phantom circuit is thus higher, with multiple twin-quads, but lower, with star quads, than that of the side circuit.

The method of line loading preferred for use in Germany today, with a loading section length $s = 1.7\,\text{km}$, makes provision for an inductance of 80 mH for the side circuit coils and an inductance of 40 mH for the phantom coils.

In other countries, where the loading section length is usually 1.83 km, provision is made for an inductance of 88 mH for the side circuit coils, and an inductance of 36 mH for the phantom coils.

In the carrier-frequency region, coil-loaded cabling can only be used with a small number of audio channels due to its low-pass effect. In such instances the inductance of the coils in the side circuit only amounts to 1 to 2 mH. Coil-loaded, carrier-frequency cables are only rarely in use today, since unloaded carrier cables connected by relatively inexpensive transistorised relay amplifiers are far more advantageous.

Loading coil sections and electrical building out networks

It is generally impossible, in practice, to locate the loading points exactly at the theoretically required positions. Moreover, the permissible tolerances in the mutual capacity along the manufactured lengths of cabling cause differences in the mutual capacity between one loading section and another. These differences, however, may not exceed specified values.

The International Advisory Committee for Telegraphy and Telephony (CCITT) recommend that, within each group of side circuit and phantom lines in a cable connection, the average mutual capacities of the individual loading sections, within the same VF repeater section, may deviate by not more than 2% from the mean value of all the loading sections in the group concerned. To express this in another way, the nominal value of the coil spacing within any repeater section must be equal to the theoretical value with a maximum tolerance in capacity of $\pm 2\%$. In addition to this requirement CCITT have ruled that the actual geometrically-measured coil spacing may deviate from the nominal value by ± 10 m at most.

These conditions are based on the fact that, in loaded lines, differences in the characteristic impedance Z, which are unduly high cause reflections which adversely affect the transmission of information, especially so in the instance of two-wire amplified lines. When the cable is laid, or when it is assembled, these requirements are satisfied by supplementary measures. The so-called balancing of capacity deviations in a cable (compensating for the operating capacities of adjacent lines) can either be achieved by *grouping the factory lengths according to their average capacity values* or by *capacitive building-out networks*.

The grouping of the lengths is generally very expensive and does not always ensure that the requirements will be observed, particularly if an originally-supplied length of cable has been incorrectly laid or if the mutual capacity, as a result of damage to the line, is altered by the replacement of a new length with an average value of mutual capacity which differs considerably from the original length. Consequently, the longitudinal balancing by means of capacitors is preferable, i.e., connecting additional capacitances into the line.

The reflections produced by deviations in the characteristic impedance Z under operating conditions must be measured, not at their point of origin but at the output or termination of the line resp. at the repeaters. This means that, as the distance between the repeater and the intersection (causing the reflection) increases, so the attenuation of the reflected waves as they reach the repeater is attenuated in proportion to the line attenuation. The economic advantage to be gained from this is used when making practical balancing for capacity deviations.

An example will reveal this more clearly. An VF repeater section 85 km in length consists of an $\frac{s}{2}$ section at the start and finish, and has 49 loading sections, each

1.7 km long. The star quads are only operated with their side circuits. The diameter of the conductors is 0.9 mm. For such trunk lines the following methods of balancing are possible, beginning at the cable inputs.

> 1.5% tolerance from load section to load section for the first five load sections (including the half section)

2% tolerance in the next five load sections
3% tolerance in the following five load sections
5% tolerance in the remaining 21 load sections.

Because it is a matter of experience that some 50% of all load sections have to be equipped with capacitors, when the tolerance in the compensation is 1.5%, this means that when applying the scheme mentioned above, only ten out of a total of 51 sections are affected and of these only five sections require capacitors.

On the other hand, if the tolerance in the local compensation of all the 51 load sections was 1.5%, then capacitors would have to be connected to some 25 sections, i.e., about five times the previous number of capacitors would need to be used.

In addition to these small deviations in the length of the load section, due mainly to capacitive tolerances and, to a lesser extent, to deviations in actual length, in practice much larger geometrical deviations from the nominal length of the load section actually occur. The cause of this is usually the fact that coil housings cannot always be installed at some specific location, due to conditions determined by the terrain (e.g., rivers etc.). Since the nominal length of the load section may not be exceeded by more than 10 m, the geometrical coil spacing is (compulsorily) reduced by the final location for the installation of the coil. Since it is also absolutely essential that the nominal electrical coil spacing should be maintained, the geometrical spacing must be supplemented by connecting so-called electrical building-out networks to the line. The necessity of building-out networks can be avoided with laying the cable in loops, where the deviations only amount to some 10 m.

The deviations from the length for the load section most often occur at the cable termination to the telephone exchange, because the finishing length is either less than or greater than $\frac{s}{2}$, being very seldom equal to $\frac{s}{2}$.

For building out up to 100 m in length of cables, the necessary electrical supplementation is achieved with capacitors. When larger lengths of cable are absent building-out networks are used. These building-out networks (or capacitors) are usually connected, locally to the cable coil and thus correct the electrical missing cable length. This means that the electrical length of the load section is produced both by the existing cable and by the building-out network. The building-out networks can also be fitted to the telephone exchange (in the instance of $\frac{s}{2}$ starting and finishing sections). If the finishing section at the telephone exchange is greater than $\frac{s}{2}$ the last coil is usually assembled to the cable at distance $\frac{s}{2}$ from the telephone exchange, and the length of cable which is then left between the penultimate and final coil is compensated with electrical building-out networks to make one complete load section.

111

6.1.3. Line constants and characteristic impedance of a coaxial pair

Because it is permissible to neglect the magnetic field within the conductor since, (as for the current density) its rapid reduction as it approaches the centre of the conductor is exponential, by reason of the skin effect, the inductance and capacitance of a coaxial pair can, therefore, be calculated as follows

$$L = \frac{\mu_0 \cdot \mu_r}{2\pi} \cdot \ln \frac{r_a}{r_i} \quad \text{and}$$

$$C = \frac{2\pi \cdot \varepsilon_0 \cdot \varepsilon}{\ln \frac{r_a}{r_i}}$$

where μ_0, the permeability of 'empty' space is $1.257 \cdot 10^{-8}$, and can be measured in the following units

$$\left(\frac{V \cdot s}{A \cdot cm} \quad \text{or} \quad \frac{\Omega \cdot s}{cm} \quad \text{or} \quad \frac{H}{cm} \right);$$

$\mu_r = 1$ (for non-magnetic material such as copper)

ε_0, the dielectric constant of empty space is $0.0886 \cdot 10^{-12}$, and can be measured in the following units

$$\left(\frac{A \cdot s}{V \cdot cm} \quad \text{or} \quad \frac{s}{\Omega \cdot cm} \quad \text{or} \quad \frac{F}{cm} \right);$$

ε is the resultant dielectric constant for the insulation between internal and external conductor (e.g., air, and PE (polyethylene) discs);

$2 \cdot r_a$ is the internal diameter of the outside conductor in mm;

$2 \cdot r_i$ is the diameter of the internal conductor in mm.

The units in practical use are $\frac{mH}{km}$ (for L) and $\frac{nF}{km}$ (for C).

As the frequency increases (after approximately 100 kHz) the characteristic impedance approximates the real value

$$Z_\infty = \sqrt{\frac{L}{C}}.$$

At an infinitely-high frequency this expression is exact, i.e., it is true for complete current displacement/skin effect.

By substituting the values for L and C given above in the equation for Z then

$$Z_\infty = \frac{60}{\sqrt{\varepsilon}} \cdot \ln \frac{r_a}{r_i};$$

Z_∞ is the characteristic impedance in ohms.

The effective resistance (per unit length), R, of a coaxial pair, for non-magnetic material (copper outer conductor applied longitudinally), is

$$R = \frac{\varrho_i}{2\pi \cdot r_i \cdot \vartheta_i} + \frac{\varrho_a}{2\pi \cdot r_a \cdot \vartheta_a}$$

where

ϱ_i is the specific resistance of the internal conductor
ϱ_a is the specific resistance of the external conductor
ϑ_i is the depth of penetration on the internal conductor
ϑ_a is the depth of penetration on the external conductor.

If the material of both conductors is the same

$$\varrho_i = \varrho_a = \varrho, \quad \text{and if} \quad \vartheta = \sqrt{\frac{\varrho}{\pi \cdot \mu_0 \cdot f}}$$

then

$$R = \sqrt{\frac{\varrho \cdot \mu_0 \cdot f}{\pi}} \cdot \left(\frac{1}{2 \cdot r_i} + \frac{1}{2 \cdot r_a} \right).$$

In the higher frequency regions, i.e., above approximately 100 kHz, the following approximation can be used for the attenuation constant

$$\alpha \approx \frac{R}{2} \sqrt{\frac{C}{L}} + \frac{G}{2} \sqrt{\frac{L}{C}} = \alpha_R + \alpha_G,$$

where α_R is the attenuation constant due to resistance and α_G is that due to leakage current.

Using the expression $Z = \sqrt{\dfrac{L}{C}}$, then

$$\alpha \approx \frac{R}{2 \cdot Z} + \frac{G \cdot Z}{2}.$$

Due to the low insulation loss factor, $\tan \delta$, the leakage current attenuation, can be disregarded in the instance of coaxial pairs insulated by a mixture of air and PE (polyethylene) discs. If both conductors are of the same material the equation for α then becomes

$$\alpha = \frac{R}{2 \cdot Z} = \frac{\sqrt{\varepsilon \cdot \pi \cdot f \cdot \varrho}}{2} \cdot \frac{\dfrac{1}{r_i} + \dfrac{1}{r_a}}{\ln \dfrac{r_a}{r_i}}.$$

113

By considering the minimum value, the lowest attenuation is obtained when the ratio $\frac{r_a}{r_i} \approx 3.6$ (which is the basis for the 1.2/4.4 and 2.6/9.5 coaxial pairs) so that the characteristic impedance becomes

$$Z = \frac{77}{\sqrt{\varepsilon}} \; .$$

It should be mentioned here that the characteristic impedance of free space (the ether, a vacuum) is

$$Z_0 = \sqrt{\frac{\mu_0}{\varepsilon_0}} \approx 377 \, \Omega \, .$$

The phase delay time, τ_p of a coaxial pair, expressed in $\frac{s}{km}$, is

$$\tau_p = \sqrt{L \cdot C} \, .$$

It is of interest that the distortions due to the group delay are only half as large as those due to the phase delay.

6.1.4. Approximation formulae for heavy open wire lines and unloaded cable lines at high frequencies (CF and coaxial)

For frequencies above approximately 100 kHz the attenuation constant α expressed in $\frac{Np}{km}$ is

$$\alpha \approx \frac{R}{2} \sqrt{\frac{C}{L}} + \frac{G}{2} \sqrt{\frac{L}{C}} = \alpha_R + \alpha_G \, .$$

In a coaxial pair, where the insulation is a combination of air and PE (polyethylene) discs, the leakage current loss can be neglected in comparison with the resistance loss. With

$$Z = \sqrt{\frac{L}{C}}, \quad \text{then } \alpha_{coax} = \frac{R}{2Z} \, .$$

In the higher frequency range, above 100 kHz, the attenuation increases with the ratio $\sqrt{\frac{f_2}{f_1}}$; where f_2 is the higher frequency for which the attenuation has to be determined, whilst f_1 is the lower frequency for which the attenuation is already known.

The phase constant (or angular constant) β expressed in $\frac{\text{rad}}{\text{km}}$ is

$$\beta = \alpha \cdot \sqrt{L \cdot C}, \qquad \text{and}$$

the characteristic impedance which, at the higher frequencies (above some 100 kHz), nearly becomes real, is

$$Z_r = \sqrt{\frac{L}{C}}.$$

Example

In a CF line with 0.9 mm conductor diameter

$$C_B = 30.9 \frac{\text{nF}}{\text{km}}$$

$$L \approx 0.7 \frac{\text{mH}}{\text{km}}.$$

Consequently,

$$Z_r = \sqrt{\frac{L}{C}} = \sqrt{\frac{0.7 \cdot 10^{-3}}{30.9 \cdot 10^{-9}}} \approx 150.2 \, \Omega.$$

The complex characteristic impedance, expressed in ohms, becomes

$$Z_L = \sqrt{\frac{L}{C}} \cdot e^{-j\varphi} \qquad \text{and}$$

$$\varphi = \frac{\varepsilon - \delta}{2}$$

since

then $\quad \tan \varepsilon = \dfrac{R}{\omega \cdot L} \quad$ and $\quad \tan \delta = \dfrac{G}{\omega \cdot C}.$

The modulus of the characteristic impedance is

$$|Z_L| = \sqrt{Z_r^2 + Z_i^2} \; ;$$

where

$$\tan \varphi = \frac{|Z_r|}{|Z_i|}, \quad j = \sqrt{-1} \quad \text{und} \quad j^2 = -1, \quad \text{then}$$

115

$$Z_r = 155\,\Omega$$

$$Z_i = -14\,\Omega \quad \text{and}$$

$$\tan\varphi = \frac{14}{155} = 0.09 \qquad \text{so that the}$$

angle $\varphi = 5°$.

The amount of the characteristic impedance is thus

$$|Z_L| = \sqrt{155^2 + 14^2} \approx 155.6\,\Omega$$

whence it becomes obvious that, at the higher frequencies, the characteristic imped-ance practically becomes a purely real quantity.

6.1.5. Approximation formulae for unloaded thin-wire cables

In cable lines the inductive line resistance $\omega \cdot L$ in the audiofrequency band (300 to 3400 Hz), is very small compared with the ohmic resistance R. The leakage con-ductance G is also small compared with the capacitance value $\omega \cdot C$. Consequently, when considering approximation formulae, $\omega \cdot L$ and G can be neglected, without any appreciable error.

The attenuation constant α, expressed in $\dfrac{\text{Np}}{\text{km}}$, is practically equal to the phase constant β, expressed in $\dfrac{\text{rad}}{\text{km}}$:

$$\alpha \approx \beta = \sqrt{\frac{R \cdot \omega \cdot C}{2}}$$

The complex characteristic impedance, in ohms, is

$$Z_L = \sqrt{\frac{R}{\omega \cdot C}} \cdot e^{-j45°} =$$

$$= \sqrt{\frac{R}{2\omega \cdot C}} - j\sqrt{\frac{R}{2\omega \cdot C}} =$$

$$= Z_r + Z_i; \qquad \text{whence}$$

$$Z_r = -Z_i = \sqrt{\frac{R}{2\omega \cdot C}}.$$

The amount of the characteristic impedance is therefore

$$|Z_L| = \sqrt{Z_r^2 + Z_i^2}$$

116

Example

The diameter of the conductors in a line is 0.8 mm. The values for R and C, actually measured were $R = 72 \, \dfrac{\Omega}{\text{km}}$, C_B side circuit $= 38 \, \dfrac{\text{nF}}{\text{km}}$. Find the characteristic impedance at a frequency of 800 Hz.

Solution:

$$\omega = 2 \cdot \pi \cdot f \approx 5030 \, s^{-1}$$

$$\alpha = \sqrt{\frac{R \cdot \omega \cdot C}{2}} = \sqrt{\frac{72 \cdot 5.030 \cdot 10^3 \cdot 38 \cdot 10^{-9}}{2}} \approx$$

$$\approx 82.6 \cdot 10^{-3} \, \frac{\text{Np}}{\text{km}} = 82.6 \, \frac{\text{mNp}}{\text{km}} \approx 0.72 \, \frac{\text{dB}}{\text{km}}$$

$$Z_r = \sqrt{\frac{R}{2 \cdot \omega \cdot C}} = \sqrt{\frac{72}{2 \cdot 5.03 \cdot 10^3 \cdot 38 \cdot 10^{-9}}} \approx$$

$$\approx 0.435 \cdot 10^3 = 435 \, \Omega = - Z_i \, ;$$

$$|Z_L| = \sqrt{Z_r^2 + Z_i^2} = \sqrt{435^2 + 435^2} \approx 615 \, \Omega.$$

6.1.6. Approximation formulae for loaded thin-wire cables

The attenuation on loaded cable lines in the useful (audio) frequency band is practically constant within the pass-band i.e., there is scarcely any increase in the attenuation within this region. The attenuation constant α, in $\dfrac{\text{Np}}{\text{km}}$, is therefore approximately:

$$\alpha = \frac{R}{2 \cdot \sqrt{\dfrac{L}{C}}} = \frac{R}{2 \cdot Z_0} \, .$$

The characteristic impedance Z_0, in ohms, is also of the resp. loaded lines and is calculated as follows:

$$Z_0 = \sqrt{\frac{L}{C}} = \sqrt{\frac{L'_K \cdot s + L_{Sp}}{C'_K \cdot s + C_{Sp}}} = Z_r \, ;$$

$$\omega_0 = \frac{2}{\sqrt{L \cdot C}} \qquad \text{or} \qquad 2\pi \cdot f_0 \, ;$$

$$f_0 = \frac{\omega_0}{2\pi} = \frac{1}{\pi \cdot \sqrt{L \cdot C}} = \frac{1}{\pi \cdot s \sqrt{\left(L'_K + \dfrac{L_{Sp}}{s}\right)\left(C'_K + \dfrac{C_{Sp}}{s}\right)}}$$

where s is the coil spacing (length of load section) in km

$$R = R'_K + \frac{R_{Sp}}{s} \text{ in } \frac{\Omega}{km}$$

(in phantom lines R'_K is only half the value of R' for the side circuit); L'_K is the inductance of the line in mH/km (this value is approximately $0.7\,\dfrac{\text{mH}}{\text{km}}$ for side circuits and $0.4\,\dfrac{\text{mH}}{\text{km}}$ on phantom lines); L_{sp} is the inductance of the loading coil in mH; C'_K is the capacitance of the line in $\dfrac{\text{nF}}{\text{km}}$; C_{SP} is the capacitance of the loading coil in nF (about 0.05 nF).

Example

Paper-insulated star quad, St-quality, conductor diameter 0.9 mm, (phantom-loaded):

where

$$C'_K \triangleq C'_{\text{cable, side circuit}} = 34 \frac{\text{nF}}{\text{km}}$$

$$C'_{\text{cable, phantom circuit}} = 92 \frac{\text{nF}}{\text{km}}$$

$$C_{Sp} \triangleq C_{\text{coil, side circuit}} = 2.5\,\text{nF}$$

$$C_{\text{coil, phantom circuit}} = 0.1\,\text{nF}$$

$$L_{Sp} \triangleq L_{\text{coil, side circuit}} = 80\,\text{mH}$$

$$L_{\text{coil, phantom circuit}} = 40\,\text{mH}$$

$$L'_K \triangleq L'_{\text{cable, side circuit}} = 0.7\,\text{mH}$$

$$L'_{\text{cable, phantom circuit}} = 0.4\,\text{mH}$$

$$R'_K \triangleq R'_{\text{cable, side circuit}} = 56.6\,\frac{\Omega}{\text{km}}$$

$$R_{Sp} \triangleq R'_{\text{coil, side circuit}} = 3.5\,\Omega$$

$$R'_{\text{coil, phantom circuit}} = 1.75\,\Omega$$

$$s \quad \text{length of loading section} = 1.7\,\text{km}$$

The characteristic impedance Z_0 of the side circuit is:

$$Z_0 = \sqrt{\frac{L'_K \cdot s + L_{Sp}}{C'_K \cdot s + C_{Sp}}} = \sqrt{\frac{(0.7 \cdot 1.7 + 80) \cdot 10^{-3}}{(34 \cdot 1.7 + 2.5) \cdot 10^{-9}}} \approx 1160\,\Omega$$

$$\alpha_{\text{side circuit}} = \frac{R}{2 \cdot Z_0} = \frac{56.6 + \dfrac{3.5}{1.7}}{2 \cdot 1160} \approx 0.0253\,\frac{\text{Np}}{\text{km}} = 25.3\,\frac{\text{mNp}}{\text{km}} \approx 0.22\,\frac{\text{dB}}{\text{km}}.$$

The characteristic impedance Z_0 of the phantom line is:

$$Z_0 = \sqrt{\frac{(0.4 \cdot 1.7 + 40) \cdot 10^{-3}}{(92 \cdot 1.7 + 0.1) \cdot 10^{-9}}} \approx 510\,\Omega$$

$$\alpha_{\text{phantom}} = \frac{\dfrac{56.6}{2} + \dfrac{1.75}{1.7}}{2 \cdot 510} \approx 0.0287\,\frac{\text{Np}}{\text{km}} = 28.7\,\frac{\text{mNp}}{\text{km}} \approx 0.25\,\frac{\text{dB}}{\text{km}}.$$

6.1.7. Conversion of test results to the reference quantities l_0 and t_0

The length l and the temperature t of the item under test usually differ from the reference length l_0 and the reference temperature t_0 (e.g., $+20\,°C$) which determine the values given in the specification. To prove that the values in the specification have been maintained, the test measurements x are then converted as stated in the table and has explained in the following example.

Table 4   Conversion of the test measurements to the reference value l_0 and t_0

Type of measurement	Conversion for length	Conversion for temperature
Loop resistance or conductor resistance	$x \cdot \dfrac{l_0}{l}$	$\dfrac{x}{1 + 4 \cdot 10^{-3}\,(t - t_0)}$
Resistance difference	$x \cdot \sqrt{\dfrac{l_0}{l}}$	
Insulation resistance (for paper insulated cable)	$x \cdot \dfrac{l}{l_0}$	$\dfrac{x}{1 - 6 \cdot 10^{-2}\,(t - t_0)}$
Mutual capacity	$x \cdot \dfrac{l_0}{l}$	
Cross-talk attenuation (Line constant of far-end cross-talk attenuation $a_f - a$) CCITT (G321)	$x + \ln \dfrac{l}{l_0} \;\; \triangleq$ addition for voltage	
Sometimes required by foreign customers	$x + \dfrac{1}{2} \ln \dfrac{l}{l_0} \triangleq$ addition for power	
Coupling (for factory lengths). Maximum for any particular value CCITT and VDE	$x \cdot \dfrac{l_0}{l}$	
Sometimes as required by foreign customers	$x \cdot \dfrac{1}{\dfrac{1}{2}\left(\dfrac{l}{l_0} + \sqrt{\dfrac{l}{l_0}}\right)}$	
Maximum for mean values VDE: k_1 CCITT: $k_{1,4\ldots12}$; $m_{1,9\ldots12}$	$x \cdot \sqrt{\dfrac{l_0}{l}}$	
CCITT: $k_{2,3}$; $e_{1\ldots3}$	$x \cdot \dfrac{l_0}{l}$	

Example for converting a particular k_1 value:

$x = 700\,\mathrm{pF}$, when measured over a length ($\,\hat{=}\,l$) of 600 m

$l_0 = 300\,\mathrm{m}$ as per German Electrical Engineering Association (VDE) and

$k_1 = 400\,\mathrm{pF}$ (maximum value for 300 m)

$700 \cdot \dfrac{300}{600} = 350\,\mathrm{pF}$; i.e., the test measured value is permissible since, when referred to $l_0 = 300$ m, it is smaller than the maximum value $k_1 = 400\,\mathrm{pF}$, which is permissible in this respect.

Calculated in another way the permissible value for 600 m is:

$400 \cdot \dfrac{600}{300} = 800\,\mathrm{pF}$.

6.2. Transmission quality of a line

Proper transmission quality can only be attained if the CCITT recommendations regarding transmission losses, distortion and noise etc., are observed on national and international communications connections, and if modern telephones are used with an efficient reduction in side tones.

Reductions in the transmission quality of a communications system are thus caused not only by power losses due to attenuation along the transmission path but also by distortion and noise. This applies even when the audio frequency band is restricted. This reduction in quality, however, becomes noticeable only when the restriction in the frequency band falls below 3400 Hz and is, for example, almost 6 dB (0.7 Np) at 2000 Hz.

6.2.1. Attenuation

The reference equivalent of an electrical communications system is the value recorded by NOSFER (New Master System for the determination of reference equivalents), when this is adjusted to be equal in volume with the system to be measured, if the same audio power is available to both systems. More precise details on reference equivalents can be obtained from 6.3.

Image attenuation constant (wave attenuation) – Bel (B) and Neper (Np)

From a consideration of the general line equations, the definition of the attenuation unit, a, in the transmission constant of a line, $g = a + jb$, is also typical of every four-terminal network. The behaviour of any four-terminal network, with any termination, $R = \dfrac{U_2}{I_2}$, can be clearly described by this constant, even if it cannot be easily measured. Terminating the four-terminal network with its characteristic impedance makes a real simplification, since the voltages at the input and output behave in the same way as do the currents.

The attenuation unit, a, of a four-terminal network (in Np) is:

$$a = \ln \frac{U_1}{U_2} \quad \text{or} \quad \ln \frac{I_1}{I_2}.$$

A Neper is not a unit, it is only an indication of the natural logarithm for a ratio, and is therefore a number. This, further, also applies to the Bel. Nepers and Bels are, however, used as units.

In English-speaking countries the attenuation unit is usually measured in Bels. This is also becoming more common in Germany. Logarithms, to the base 10, are used for Bels whilst natural logarithm are used for Nepers.

Therefore:

$$a = 2 \lg \frac{U_1}{U_2} \quad \text{or} \quad 2 \lg \frac{I_1}{I_2} \text{ in Bels (B)}$$

and

$$a = 20 \lg \frac{U_1}{U_2} \quad \text{or} \quad 20 \lg \frac{I_1}{I_2} \text{ in Decibels (dB)}.$$

The following equations give the conversions:

$$
\begin{aligned}
1 \text{ Neper (Np)} &= 0.8686 \text{ Bels (B)} = 8.686 \text{ Decibels (dB)} \\
1 \text{ B} &= 1.151 \text{ Np} \\
1 \text{ dB} &= 0.1151 \text{ Np}.
\end{aligned}
$$

The attenuation unit is also derived from the ratio (see the definition of a Bel)

$$a = \frac{1}{2} \ln \frac{P_1}{P_2} \text{ in Np or} \quad a = 10 \lg \frac{P_1}{P_2} \text{ in dB},$$

where

$P_1 = U_1 \cdot I_1$ the primary (input) power and

$P_2 = U_2 \cdot I_2$ the secondary (output) power

of the four-terminal network (line or system).

Another term for the attenuation constant a is the *relative voltage level* or *relative power level*. The relative level indicates the number of Np or dB by which the voltage or power at the tested point (Index 2) is less than the voltage or power at the reference point (Index 1).

With reference to the idea of "level" it is generally true that

$$p = -a.$$

If the voltage at the input is, for example, $2.718 = e^1$ times greater than the voltage at the output, then the attenuation is 1 Np. When $e^2 = 2$ Np the voltages at input and output differ by a factor of 7.39. Further values are:

$$
\begin{aligned}
e^0 &= 0 \ \mathrm{Np} = \text{factor of} & 1 & \quad \text{(unattenuated)} \\
e^{0.5} &= 0.5 \ \mathrm{Np} = \text{factor of} & 1.65 & \\
e^3 &= 3 \ \mathrm{Np} = \text{factor of} & 20.1 & \\
e^5 &= 5 \ \mathrm{Np} = \text{factor of} & 148.0 & \\
e^7 &= 7 \ \mathrm{Np} = \text{factor of} \approx 1000 & \\
e^8 &= 8 \ \mathrm{Np} = \text{factor of} & 2980 & \\
e^{10} &= 10 \ \mathrm{Np} = \text{factor of} & 20000. &
\end{aligned}
$$

Conversely, for the voltage, a factor of

$$
\begin{aligned}
10 &= e^{2.3} = 2.3 \ \mathrm{Np} = 20 \ \mathrm{dB} \\
100 &= e^{4.6} = 4.6 \ \mathrm{Np} = 40 \ \mathrm{dB} \\
1000 &= e^{6.9} = 6.9 \ \mathrm{Np} = 60 \ \mathrm{dB}.
\end{aligned}
$$

For power a value of e.g. $+10 \ \mathrm{dB}$ corresponds to a factor of 10, whilst a value of $-10 \ \mathrm{dB}$ gives a factor of 0.1. Take, for example, an amplification in the ratio $1:10000 = 10 \cdot 10 \cdot 10 \cdot 10 = 10^4$. Corresponding to this there is a value of $4 \cdot 10 \ \mathrm{dB} = 40 \ \mathrm{dB} \approx 4.6 \ \mathrm{Np}$. Because they can be stated in multiples of ten it is preferable to give attenuation data in dB.

It is normal practice to use the abbreviations Np for neper, dB for decibel, V for volt (voltage) and pW for pico watt (noise power) output with supplements, e.g. dBm, which have the following meanings:

m   relative to a power of 1 mW

r   relative level

0   relative to a point with a relative level of 0 Np or 0 dB

p   evaluated according to CCITT in relation to the sensitivity of the human ear at various frequencies.

Operative attenuation

In actual practice only an approximation to the unreflected termination ($R = Z$) of a line can be achieved, over the whole frequency range, with simple means such as ohmic resistances.

Fig. 26   Illustration of the operative attenuation unit

Consequently, instead of the image attenuation constant, a new term of attenuation has been created, namely the *operative attenuation unit*, a_B measured in Np, which can also be easily measured. It is defined by the following relationship:

$$a_B = \frac{1}{2} \ln \frac{P_0}{P_2} \text{ resp. in dB} = 10 \lg_{10} \frac{P_0}{P_2}.$$

In this equation P_0 is the apparent power that could be supplied by a generator, with an open-circuit a.c. voltage U_0 and an internal resistance R_i, to an external resistance, R_1, of equal value. P_2 is the apparent power which the generator delivers, when connected into a four-terminal network, to the terminating resistor R_2.

The operative attenuation unit can therefore be represented, as is the usual method in actual practice, by

$$a_B = \lg \frac{\frac{U_0}{2}}{U_2} + \frac{1}{2} \lg \frac{R_2}{R_1} \text{ in Np resp.} = 20 \lg \frac{\frac{U_0}{2}}{U_2} + 10 \lg \frac{R_2}{R_1} \text{ in dB}$$

and is a criterium for the attenuation of any terminated four-terminal network.

It is important for international telephone traffic that the operation attenuation unit should be measured according to some uniform standard. For this purpose the quantities U_0, P_0, and R_i have been established (by CCITT) as having the widest application in practical conditions.

For the purposes of measurement a *standard generator* is used which, with a real internal resistance, $R_i = 600\,\Omega$, supplies a power, $P_0 = 1\,\text{mW}$, to an external resistance, R_1, of equal value i.e., $R_1 = R_i$. The open-circuit voltage is thus 1.55 V, and the current, delivered by the generator is 1.29 mA. The voltage across R_1 is therefore

$$0.775\,\text{V} \triangleq 600\,\Omega \cdot 0.00129\,\text{A}.$$

If a voltage of 0.5 V is measured at the output of the four-terminal network, when terminated with a resistor $R_2 = 1200\,\Omega$, then the operative attenuation unit is:

$$a_B = 20 \lg \frac{\frac{1.55}{2}}{0.5} + 10 \lg \frac{1200}{600} = 6.8\,\text{dB} \approx 0.78\,\text{Np}.$$

123

The voltage U_x, the current I_x, and the power P_x at any point x along a line are generally referred to the values of the standard generator. For this reason the values U_0, I_0, P_0 are known as the zero-voltage/current/power level.

The ratio of the voltage U_x, at any point at a distance x from the beginning of the line, to the output/transmitted voltage $\frac{U_0}{2} = 0.775$ V, is called the *absolute voltage level*,

$$p_s = \ln \frac{U_x}{0.775} \text{ in Np resp.} = 20 \lg \frac{U_x}{0.775} \text{ in dB}.$$

Voltages less than 0.775 thus correspond to a "negative" voltage level. For example, if $U_x = 0.0387\ V$ then the absolute voltage level at this point x along the line is:

$$p_s = 20 \lg \frac{0.0387}{0.775} \approx 20 \lg 0.05 = -26 \text{ dB or} \approx -3 \text{ Np}.$$

The ratio of the power P_x, at a point distant x from the beginning of the line to the output (transmitted) power, $P_0 = \frac{U_0}{2} I_0 = 0.775 \cdot 1.29 \approx 1$ mW, characterises the absolute power level,

$$p_m = \frac{1}{2} \ln \frac{P_x}{1\,\text{mW}} \text{ in Np resp.} = 10 \lg \frac{P_x}{1\,\text{mW}} \text{ in dB}.$$

The following equation expresses the relationship between the power level p and the line loss unit a_B: $p = -a_B$. However, here it is assumed that the line loss unit has been ascertained with a standard generator ($R_i = 600\,\Omega$). When the terminating resistor R_2 is equal to the internal resistance $R_i = R_1$, then the line loss unit becomes the over-all attenuation unit, a_R

$$a_R = \ln \frac{\frac{U_0}{2}}{U_2} \text{ in Np resp.} = 20 \lg \frac{U_1}{U_2} \text{ in dB}.$$

Cross-talk attenuation

Cross-talk is associated with the concept of attenuation. The *cross-talk attenuation unit* a_N, is:

$$a_N = \ln \frac{U_1}{U_2} \text{ in Np resp.} = 20 \lg \frac{U_1}{U_2} \text{ in dB},$$

provided that the terminating impedances Z_1 and Z_2 are equal. U_1 is the voltage at the transmitter and U_2 is the measured disturbing voltage.

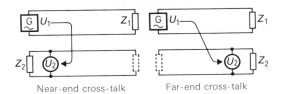

Fig. 27
Near-end and far-end
cross-talk

Near-end cross-talk Far-end cross-talk

When the resistance $Z_2 \neq Z_1$, the cross-talk attenuation unit is defined with reference to the effective line loss as:

$$a_N = \frac{1}{2} \ln \frac{P_1}{P_2} = \ln \frac{U_1}{U_2} + \frac{1}{2} \ln \frac{Z_2}{Z_1} \text{ in Np resp.} = 10 \lg \frac{P_1}{P_2} \text{ in dB}.$$

More precise details on cross-talk are given in 6.4.

Return loss

The *return loss unit* is defined as

$$a_F = \lg \frac{W + Z}{W - Z} \text{ in Np resp.} = 20 \lg \frac{W + Z}{W - Z} \text{ in dB}$$

where W is the resistance of the balance network in ohms; Z is the characteristic impedance of the line in ohms.

In telecommunications cables the idea of balance attenuation is an important factor in proving that a high quality cable has been correctly constructed and designed (e.g., a loaded VF-line). The balance attenuation must be not less than 26 dB (3 Np). Any lesser value suggests that, on a loaded line for example,

- a coil is missing
- a coil has been wrongly included or the mutual capacity of a loading section deviates from the specified value through excessive supplementation
- the mutual capacity of a loading coil section differs from the necessary value by compensation or through a faulty network (capacitor).

The *matching attenuation*, the *structural return loss*, the *reflection attenuation* (attenuation of the reflected current), and the *echo attenuation* are similarly defined. Basically, the problem dealt with here is the evaluation of the amount of *mismatching* i.e., varying values of the characteristic impedance, either of lines inter-connected together or connected by amplifiers.

The associated mismatching factor, also known as the *reflection factor*, expressed as a percentage is:

$$r = \frac{W - Z}{W + Z} \cdot 100 .$$

where r is the reflection factor in %.

When transmitting television along coaxial pairs the unfavourable effect of an excessive pulse (surge) is particularly noticeable. Here it is a problem of several reflected waves at the amplifiers or at other junction points (impedance variations from cable length to cable length or changes in the impedance of a coaxial pair due to variations in its dimensions). When assessed in conjunction with the carrier frequency of the TV systems, these reflected waves can cause a "*blip*" on the picture screen. The reflected wave is again reflected by the earlier impedance variations (amplifiers) in the direction of transmission and becomes superimposed with a phase lag in the direction of the useful wave. In such instances it must be taken into consideration that the first reflected wave is also attenuated in proportion to the line loss ($\alpha \cdot l$).

6.2.2. Distortion

An electrically-transmitted signal is also typified by its frequency band (its complete spectrum of frequencies). The changes in the frequency spectrum of a message as it travels along the transmission system are termed by the *distortions* which are distinguished as linear and non-linear distortions.

Linear distortions

Linear distortions occur in linear systems. These distortions are dependent upon the transmission properties of the system which can be described in terms of attenuation or phase. A signal is transmitted along a line without any distortion, if the spectrum of amplitudes in the signal transmitted to the input of the line is received unaltered at the output of the line. If the signal contains partial oscillations of frequency $0...\omega_0$ then, for distortionless transmission of the signal, it is necessary that, within the transmission band ($0...\omega_0$), the voltage and current should be unaffected by frequency during their transmission. For an ideal (distortionless) transmission system the *transmission factor* must be a constant

$$\ddot{U}_{(0...\omega_0)} = \text{constant.}$$

If the transmission properties of a line are expressed in terms of attenuation then obviously the same condition holds for a distortionless system;

$$a_{(0...\omega_0)} = \text{constant .}$$

In actual practice the transmission properties of any line deviate from these ideal assumptions.

The line loss in a non-loaded line is greater at higher frequencies than at the lower limit of the transmission range (e.g., 300 to 3400 Hz), i.e., the amplitudes of the higher frequency oscillations suffer much greater attenuation than the amplitudes of the lower frequency oscillations. This phenomenon which involves a change in the sound pattern of the signal, is called *attenuation* or *amplitude distortion* and is expressed as *a* in the frequency response for the attenuation constant. Amplitude distortions in transmission lines with repeaters are balanced out in such a way that the frequency response of the amplifier is matched to the frequency response of the line loss with the result that the higher frequencies receive greater amplification than the lower frequencies. This process is described as *attenuation equalisation*. In loaded AF lines the attenuation frequency response within the useful frequency band (approximately 300 Hz up to $\leq 75\%$ of the limiting frequency) is practically constant, i.e., within the transmission range practically no attenuation distortion occurs in such lines. The requirements are valid for the *effectively transmitted frequency band*. "Effectively transmitted" implies that the net loss at the frequency under consideration, f_x, within the frequency band (see 6.2.1.) differs from the net loss at 800 Hz by not more than 8.7 dB (1 Np).

When discussing *phase distortions* it is wiser to start with the propagation time of the waves along the transmission range. To travel through a section of line of 1 km length the propagation time required by the separate oscillations, of frequency $0 \ldots \omega_0$, contained in the signal, expressed in s/km is:

$$\tau_p = \frac{\beta}{\omega}$$

where β is the phase constant in $\frac{\text{rad}}{\text{km}}$; and ω is the angular frequency in $\frac{1}{\text{s}}$.

If the partial oscillations in the signal are to be repeated at the end of the line as they were delivered to its input then the phase relationship of the partial oscillations must be maintained. This will happen if the propagation time τ_p for all the oscillations within the transmission range is equally large. The propagation time of all the oscillations, known as the *group delay* denoted by τ_p and expressed in s/km is

$$\tau_p = \tau_g = \frac{\beta}{\omega} = \text{constant} .$$

The human ear cannot hear small distortions. If the differences in propagation time are large (> 50 ms) there is a considerable reduction in syllabic intelligibility (through interference by extraneous high-frequency noise) with the result that phase compensation is required by means of four-terminal networks, with reciprocal propaga-

127

tion time characteristics. Such differences in propagation time do not generally occur in national telephone traffic.

Non-linear distortions

Non-linear distortions occur in non-linear systems. If an oscillation of frequency f is delivered to the input of a non-linear system then in addition to the transmitted oscillation f, oscillations of frequency $2f$, $3f$, ...nf are also received which cause a change in the sound picture.

The unit for the evaluation of the non-linear distortions in a transmission system is known as the (harmonic) *distortion factor* K, which is defined as:

$$K = \frac{\text{Effective sum of all the harmonics}}{\text{Effective sum of the fundamental oscillation} + \text{all the harmonics}} \, .$$

If U_1, U_2, U_3...U_n are the effective voltages of the fundamental oscillation and the harmonics of frequency f, $2f$, $3f$...nf, then the distortion factor is:

$$K = \frac{\sqrt{U_2^2 + U_3^2 + ... U_n^2}}{\sqrt{U_1^2 + U_2^2 + ... U_n^2}}$$

then the harmonic distortion expressed as an attenuation is:

$$a_K = \ln \sqrt{\frac{U_1^2 + U_2^2 + ... U_n^2}{U_2^2 + U_3^2 + ... U_n^2}} \text{ in Np resp.} = 20 \lg \sqrt{\frac{U_1^2 + U_2^2 + ... U_n^2}{U_2^2 + U_3^2 + ... U_n^2}} \text{ in dB} \, .$$

In telephone transmissions the human ear is not generally affected by harmonic distortions where $K \leq 5\%$.

If, however, several oscillations of varying frequencies are applied to the input of a non-linear system as is true of the frequency spectrum of a signal then, besides the above-mentioned harmonics, summation and intermodulation frequencies are also produced, and these can cause serious interference in the original sound picture.

Non-linear distortions are due, on loaded lines to the inductances (Pupin coils) interposed in the line, and on lines with relay sections, to the relay amplifiers. The relationships between the input and output of a homogeneous line are linear. Consequently the phase and attenuation distortions can only be linear in such a line.

The harmonic distortion has only a slight effect on the syllabic intelligibility. When the harmonic distortion factor is as much as 10% the reduction in the syllable intelligibility is less than 3%.

6.2.3. Noises

The transmission quality of a communications system can be preceptibly affected by *noise*. The following different types of noise can be distinguished as follows:

Room noise, i.e., the noises within the room, audible at the telephone position,

Microphone noise, i.e., the noise produced by the microphone (transmitter unit),

Line noise, which includes all the transmitted noises with the exception of the room and the microphone noise.

Line noise is further classified as:

Amplifier noise, produced by the relay amplifiers,

Power induced noise, i.e., noise produced by the electrical influence of high power installations such as, for example, high-tension transmission lines and railway installations.

Intelligible (linear) cross-talk, caused by telephone currents which "trespass" from the interfering telephone circuit into the disturbed circuit (without shifting the frequency band).

Unintelligible (non linear) cross-talk, caused by telephone currents in which the frequency band has been shifted before or after "trespassing" from the interfering into the disturbed circuit (carrier frequency or secrecy systems).

Babbling, due to multiple simultaneous cross-talk.

Noise, due to oscillatory processes in the transmission system.

Scratchy noise, produced by poor contacts in the line or on the dial or because of variable insulation faults on the line.

Power supply noise, produced by the power supplies for the relay amplifiers and the microphones (whether from local or central batteries).

Clicking/acoustic shock, caused, for example, by the sudden discharge of a capacitor or by switching operations.

Telegraphic noise, due to telegraphic equipment operated on the same lines or on different lines within the same wire units.

Every interference effect in communications systems (i.e., every voltage so impressed on the communications system) produced by extraneous systems, such as high-voltage lines and the power-supply equipment for the relay amplifiers, behaves like an interference voltage (extraneous voltage or noise voltage).

The interference effect is thus greatly influenced by the harmonics in the interference voltage. Any interference voltage which can be evaluated by *psophometric curves* is denoted as psophometric or *noise voltage* (various psophometric curves have been defined by CCITT for telephone and radio lines). An unevaluated interference voltage is often simply styled *external voltage*.

The interference voltage is generally related to the useful voltage (transmitting level). Consequently, the demands for interference-free transmission are lowest in telegraphy, and are highest in radio broadcasting. The attenuation due to interference, which can be derived from the so called voltage ratio, is known as the *signal-to-noise ratio*, which is:

$$a_G = \ln \frac{U_N}{U_G} \text{ in Np resp.} = 20 \lg \frac{U_N}{U_G} \text{ in dB}$$

where a_G is the signal-to-noise ratio (attenuation due to noise); U_N is the useful voltage in Volts; U_G is the noise voltage in mV measured on a line terminated with a real resistance of 600 Ω.

The permissible values for the signal-to-noise ratio must generally correspond to the values specified for the cross-talk attenuation.

On the assumption that noises are adding with respect to power it is preferable to use the idea of *noise output* (P_G), which is defined as follows:

$$P_G = \frac{U_G^2}{Z}.$$

The noise e.m.f. of a short, unterminated telephone line is twice the value of the noise voltage measured at the end of a line terminated with a real load-terminating resistance Z of 600 Ω (at a frequency of 800 Hz), provided that the other end of the line is terminated by its characteristic impedance.

The unit used in practice for measuring the noise output is the picowatt (pW = 10^{-12} W).

When taking the noise output into consideration, the planned output for long-distance connecting cables is based upon a *reference circuit*. This reference circuit is an imaginary telephone circuit 2500 km long and which contains a specified number of terminal and intermediate equipment. This number is selected to suit the specific system (VF/CF- or Coaxial Systems), but is not the largest possible number.

The average noise output evaluated at the end of a VF-channel, the design of which corresponds to that of the reference circuit, when converted to the relative zero signal level may both not exceed 10000 pW during any hourly period.

How the total noise is distributed between background noise, intermodulation noise and noise due to cross-talk is left to the designers, but the maximum value of 2500 pW for the terminal installations, and 7500 pW for the line, may not be exceeded.

6.2.4. Side-tones

Side-tones are produced because the sound pressure absorbed by the microphone is repeated through the earphone on the same unit. A distinction is made between side-tones due to speech and those due to room noise.

There are various ways in which the performance of a conversation is hindered by side-tones. It can induce unduly loud, or quiet speech, and is annoying to the person actually speaking whilst the listener suffers interference from room noise, even when using double earphones.

6.3. Reference equivalent

The transmission properties of a telephone communications system can be subjectively defined by means of the concepts of *reference equivalent*. This means that the loudness/volume of the speech received in the earphone is compared with the loudness/volume of the speech transmitted into the microphone. For the standard unit of reference equivalent a "standard communications system" has been established by CCITT, which is referred to as NOSFER (New Master System for the determination of reference equivalents). The circuit comprises a transmitter and receiver of specified high quality connected to one another via an (ideal) standard line ($Z = 600\,\Omega$). Under such conditions the transmission of the frequency band is practically distortionless. This telephonic master reference system has zero reference equivalent. This reference equivalent corresponds, in a free sound field, to direct speech from mouth to ear at a distance of 4.35 cm.

The reference equivalent of a telephone communications system is the value recorded on the standard circuit when this is set to the same receiver volume as the system to be measured, and when the same AF power output is available at the inputs of both systems.

CCITT, in 1964, established a maximum value of 36 dB (4.2 Np) for the reference equivalent between two subscribers in the same continent, as that value at which sufficient syllabic resp. sentence intelligibility is ensured within the limits of the audio frequency band 0.3 to 3.4 kHz. This reference equivalent corresponds, in a free sound field, to speech direct from the mouth of the speaker to a single earphone when they are separated by exactly 3 m, and at 10 m distance when listening with two ears. The interference effect of room noise is almost entirely reduced by stereophonic hearing which is not possible in telephone operation.

This reference equivalent of 36 dB (4.2 Np) can be broken down into

- that due to the national system between the speaking subscriber (IN/S) and the foreign-calls exchange, A (main exchange) $\approx$ 20.8 dB (2.4 Np), denoted as the sending reference equivalent (SRE)

- that due to the national system between the listening subscriber (S) and the foreign calls exchange, B (main exchange) $\approx$ 12.2 dB (1.4 Np) denoted as the receiving reference equivalent (RRE) and

- that due to the inter-state system (international line), which almost without exception uses a four-wire connection between the respective foreign call exchanges A and B, equal to 0 $\pm$ 3 dB (0.36 Np). This value of 0 $\pm$ 3 dB represents the maximum permissible reference equivalent on the international line which results from the permissible attenuation of six sections of an international line each of 0.5 dB (0.06 Np).

The German Federal Postal and Telegraph Authority (DBP), accepting the maximum permissible reference equivalent recommended by CCITT, has developed its own attenuation system, which allots the attenuation values in the following way.

- *Sending reference equivalent* (SRE) between the subscriber, who is speaking, and his local telephone exchange (OVst/LTE), including the feeding circuit ≤ 10.3 dB (1.2 Np)

- Reference equivalent between the two local telephone exchanges (OVst/LTE) ≤ 19 dB (2.2 Np)

- *Receiving reference equivalent* (RRE) between the listening subscriber and the local telephone exchange (OVst/LTE) including the feeding circuit ≤ 1.7 dB (0.2 Np)

- for a private branch exchange at each end of the line additionally 2.5 dB $= 2 \cdot 2.5$ dB ≤ 5 dB (0.6 Np)

Total reference equivalent ≤ 36 dB (4.2 Np)

This attenuation arrangement is shown in greater detail in Fig. 28.

The following constituents contribute to the reference equivalent. The efficiency of the electroacoustic converters (transmitter and receiver units), the attenuation of the power supplies, the effective attenuation in the line and the exchange loss at the exchanges.

Sending reference equivalent

The sending reference equivalent is the reference equivalent from the subscriber who is speaking, up to the local exchange (OVst/LTE). This consists of the sending reference equivalent due to the transmitter unit, the line loss unit, $\alpha \cdot l$, of the local connecting line (see Table 6 for the values of α), the power-supply losses between the transmitter unit and the location of the *central battery*, which is generally included in the exchange and the *loss of the local exchange*. The *exchange loss* at the local exchange is approximately 1 dB. When using a central battery of approximately 60 V, the attenuation of the power supply amounts to approximately 4 dB per 1000 ohm of loop resistance.

The following transmitter units are inserted by the DBP:

Marking color:	blue	green	red
SRE in Np:	+0.2	−0.2	−0.6

         increasing volume. →

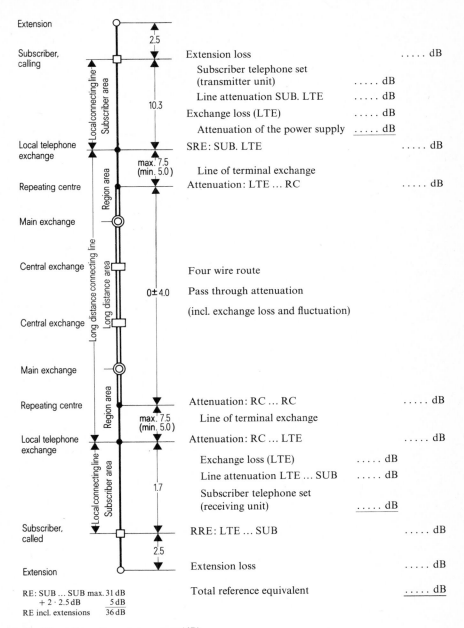

RE: SUB ... SUB max. 31 dB
  + 2 · 2.5 dB   5 dB
RE incl. extensions 36 dB

Fig. 28 Attenuation arrangement (dB)
(with four-wire operation between the repeating centres)

If the microphones are of higher standard the quality of an existing local connecting line is improved or where the local network has been replanned, lines of greater length can be used or lines with a greater attenuation constant may be installed.

In addition to the conditions for the reference equivalent there exists a relationship between the voltage of the central battery and the maximum permissible ohmic resistance in the line from the subscriber's telephone unit to his central battery.

Voltage of Central Battery in V	Loop resistance in Ω
24	400... 500
48	400...1000
60	400...1250

Table 5
Permissible ohmic resistance of the line between subscriber and central battery

The idea of *operational range* is commonly used to describe the limiting value of the loop resistance in the local connecting line. This means that, as a result of line resistance losses and also because of the microphones (transmitter units) requirements the range of the local connecting line is limited by the range of the usual selector systems and that, if, under certain circumstances, the *line losses* are excessive, the the power supply for the line can no longer be maintained within the permissible range.

The idea behind the planning of the German Federal Postal and Telegraph Authority is, when having heavily-concentrated local-subscriber lines, to install the local exchange in the centre of the subscriber network.

The result of this is that the connecting lines between the subscriber and the local exchange are relatively short. In such instances full advantage is not taken of the portion of the sending reference equivalent allotted to the line attenuation. Because the line attenuation is not as seriously altered by the conductor diameter as the associated loop resistance, the subscriber's lines are generally dimensioned with respect to the operational range i.e., with respect to the loop resistance. This also explains the tendency to use 0.4 mm conductors for the subscriber's lines.

By using transistor microphones (low-supply-current) and/or one of the more recent selector systems, the operational range can be increased to a loop resistance of as much as $1250\,\Omega$ to $1800\,\Omega$ when using 60 V central batteries. The cross-talk attenuation of local connecting cables necessarily increases with the use of loud microphones and earphones.

Reference equivalent

The *reference equivalent* (RE) between two local exchanges can be divided into the following sections.

The section from the local exchange to the repeating centre, with a maximum attenuation of 7.5 dB (0.85 Np), which is determined by the exchange and line loss, and the section covering the repeating centre, to the main exchange and central exchange through to the other central exchange, main exchange and repeater centre, with an attenuation of 0 ± 4 dB $(0 \pm 0.5$ Np). In addition to loaded and, sometimes, AF lines with relay amplifiers, this section is predominantly operated with four-wire CF lines (symmetrical or coaxial). The through line attenuation of the transmission system should be zero, with a permissible fluctuation of ± 4 dB $(\pm 0.5$ Np). This characteristic path, from the repeater centre via the main exchange to the central exchange is being more and more frequently supplemented with trunk lines such as, for example, between the repeater centre and its neighbouring main exchange.

Receiving reference equivalent

Receiving reference equivalent (RRE) covers reference equivalent between the listening subscriber and the local exchange. It consists of receiving reference equivalent in the receiver unit, the line loss unit, $\alpha \cdot l$, in the local connection cable (see Table 6 for the values of α), and the exchange loss (approx. 1 dB). There is no supply current attenuation in this instance since the power supply is only connected to the transmitter unit.

The following receiver units are inserted by the DBP:

Marking color:	blue	green	red
RRE in Np:	-0.45	-0.75	-1.5

$$\longrightarrow$$

increasing volume

If the earphones are of higher standard the transmission quality can be improved for an existing local connecting line, or where the local network has been replanned, lines of greater lengths can be used or lines with a greater attenuation constant may be installed.

Subscriber's extensions

In the instance of officially-approved subscriber's extensions (which includes the extension, the connecting line, and the exchange for the extension) and in the instance of shunt lines (first extension – connecting line – second extension) the values of sending reference equivalent 10.3 dB (1.2 Np) and receiving reference equivalent 1.7 dB (0.2 Np) as laid down for the main connections (local exchange to subscriber), in each instance, must not be exceeded by more than 2.5 dB (0.3 Np). Insofar as they are not connected to the DBP telephone network, this conception does not affect private telecommunications systems. If, however, by agreement with the German Federal Telephone Authority subscriber lines in private systems are connected to the DBP network then the attenuation values allotted to subscriber extensions must, on principle, be maintained. If the lines are not loaded it may be advisable to use NLT amplifiers (negative line resistance with transistors). These are connected to the private installation and/or to the subscriber's line of the DBP. The maximum amplification that can be taken advantage of with NLT installations is approximately (–) 7 dB (0.8 Np) at 800 Hz.

On any local connection line (subscriber to local exchange or viceversa) the sending reference equivalent and the receiving reference equivalent must be considered separately due to the difference in their values, since the subscriber who is speaking is also listening and, conversely, the subscriber at the receiver end is also speaking. No supply current flows to the receiver, and in relation to the NOSFER reference system, the attenuation in the receiver circuit is less than that in the transmitter circuit. For both reasons the closer tolerance is thus critical for subscriber's lines.

In addition to these conditions it is a requirement, as a result of CCITT recommendations, that any telephone line between two local exchanges should "efficiently" transmit a frequency band of 0.3 to 3.4 kHz. This means that the net loss at the marginal frequencies of 0.3 and 3.4 kHz does not exceed the net loss at 800 Hz by more than 8.7 dB (1 Np). On AF lines between two local exchanges, only the upper marginal frequency, 3.4 kHz, is critical. But a distinction has to be made, here, between loaded and unloaded lines.

With an unloaded connecting line the reference equivalent is approximately the same as the line attenuation at 1.3 kHz (i.e., some 30% above the line attenuation at 800 Hz).

Since the attenuation of an unloaded line increases more steeply as the frequency increases, the amplitude distortion at 3.4 kHz must also be investigated. The line loss at this frequency is approximately twice as great as at 800 Hz.

It can generally be considered that the permissible amplitude distortion of 8.7 dB may be exceeded in circumstances where the pure line loss exceeds the value of 8.7 dB at 800 Hz. It is then advisable, to load the lines with coils, to compensate them, even if the current reference equivalent can be maintained without loading.

Where a loaded line is without relay amplifiers the amplitude distortion within the useful frequency band (300 to approx. 75% of the limiting frequency) is very slight. On a loaded line, for example, with a loading section of length $s = 1.7$ km, and a coil inductance, $L_{sp} = 80$ mH, the amplitude distortion at the marginal frequency of 3.4 kHz is less than 0.035 dB/km (4 mNp/km). In such an instance the permissible value of 8.7 dB is only exceeded when the length of the line is 250 km. Because a line of such length must have relay amplifiers to observe the attenuation arrangement (or the reference equivalent between the local exchanges), it must also be compensated. The range of loaded connecting lines is thus dependent only on the reference equivalent.

Table 6   Electrical properties of side circuit lines

Conductor Diameter d, in mm	Maximum Loop Resistance R at 20 °C in Ω/km	Minimum Insulation Resistance R_{is} in $G\Omega \cdot$ km	Line Inductance L in mH/km	Mutual Capacitance C in nF/km	Attenuation Constant (at 800 Hz) in dB (mN/km) (designed value)	Value of Characteristic Impedance Z_L (at 800 Hz) in Ω

Unloaded cables

Paper-insulated; St III (star stranding)

				Max. Value		
0.4	300	5	0.7	38	1.3 (150)	1330
0.6	130	5	0.7	42	0.91 (105)	810
0.8	73.2	5	0.7	42	0.70 (80)	605

Solid PE-insulated: St III   Max. Value

0.4	300	5	0.7	50	1.49 (172)	1120
0.6	130	5	0.7	52	1.04 (120)	740
0.8	73.2	5	0.7	55	0.78 (90)	530

Paper-insulated; St I   Nominal Value

0.9	56.6	10	0.7	34	0.57 (65)	575
1.2	31.8	10	0.7	35	0.45 (52)	425
1.4	23.4	10	0.6	36	0.39 (45)	360

Loaded cables

Loaded side circuit line, paper-insulated star quads
$L_{Sp} = 140$ mH; $s = 1.7$ km; $f_0 = 3400$ Hz; useful frequency ≈ 2.6 kHz

				Nominal Value		
0.9	(56.6 + 5*)	10	(140/s + 0.7)	34	0.18 (20)	1540
1.2	(31.8 + 5*)	10	(140/s + 0.7)	35	0.12 (13)	1515
1.4	(23.4 + 5*)	10	(140/s + 0.7)	36	0.10 (11)	1495

$L_{Sp} = 80$ mH; $s = 1.7$ km; $f_0 = 4600$ Hz; useful frequency ≈ 3.4 kHz

				Nominal Value		
0.9	(56.6 + 3.5*)	10	(80/s + 0.7)	34	0.22 (25)	1160
1.2	(31.8 + 3.5*)	10	(80/s + 0.7)	35	0.14 (15)	1140
1.4	(23.4 + 3.5*)	10	(80/s + 0.6)	36	0.11 (12)	1130

*) Fraction due to coil in Ω/km

When using carrier frequency systems the net loss at 800 Hz is used as the basis for calculations when considering the reference equivalent, for the reason that, in this instance, it can be assumed that the CF-sections have been so designed, and have had their levels so adjusted, that each channel is satisfactory compensated and that at all frequencies the net loss between the AF terminals lies within the limits recommended by CCITT.

With short subscriber lines it is not generally necessary to consider distortion at the marginal frequencies. Because the reference equivalent in the line is only a fraction of the sending or receiving reference equivalent, the line loss at 800 Hz can be calculated, instead of the loss at 1.3 kHz, without any appreciable error. At the upper marginal frequency of 3.4 kHz the distortion on short subscriber lines is also insignificant, and is partially compensated by the frequency characteristic of the microphone (or earphone).

For private intercommunications networks, and for other telecommunications lines which are not responsible to DBP, a volume loss of 36 dB (4.2 Np) should not as far as possible, be exceeded, if sufficient syllabic and sentence intelligibility is to be ensured. As is clear from the foregoing, loaded lines or lines also equipped with relay amplifiers must have a far lower reference equivalent (only about 8.7 dB at 800 Hz) to observe the conditions regarding distortion. When determining the operational range, this is decided, for simple telephone lines between subscribers, on the basis of the loop resistance permissible in each instance (which is a function of the power supply current and the feeding circuit in the exchange section). This, therefore, is the explanation for the use of conductors with minimum diameter of 0.6 mm, mostly 0.8 mm in the installation of private customers.

6.4. Cross-talk

In telecommunications engineering *cross-talk* is the "trespassing" of electrical energy for one way of communication to another. In symmetrical lines, cross-talk occurs because each line, whether conducting voltage or current, produces a magnetic field which transfers a portion of the transmitted energy to other lines.

Cross-talk voltages always appear at both ends of line subject to interference. The cross-talk voltage which appears, in relation to the transmitter, at the near end of the line subject to interference is known as *near-end cross-talk*, and that which appears at the further end as *far-end cross-talk*.

Where the line causing the interference and the line subject to interference are carrying transmissions in opposite directions – such as, for example, in four-wire operation – near-end cross-talk is, in practice, much the more serious. On the other hand where the transmission along the lines are in the same direction, far-end cross-talk is the more serious (as in two-wire operation, or, where the transmissions are in the same direction, in four-wire operation).

The concept of *cross-talk attenuation*, also sometimes called transverse attenuation, is used to determine the amount of cross-talk. The unit of cross-talk attenuation is defined as the ratio between two apparent powers;

$$a_N = \frac{1}{2}\ln\frac{P_1}{P_2} \text{ in Np resp.} = \frac{1}{2}\cdot 20\lg\frac{P_1}{P_2} \text{ in dB}.$$

If the line causing the interference is terminated by its characteristic impedance Z_1 and the line subject to interference is terminated by its characteristic impedance Z_2 then

$$a_N = \ln\frac{U_1}{U_2} + \frac{1}{2}\ln\frac{Z_2}{Z_1} \text{ in Np resp.} = 20\lg\frac{U_1}{U_2} + 10\lg\frac{Z_2}{Z_1} \text{ in dB}.$$

Normally, the same type of lines in a cable have characteristic impedances which can be considered equal. The small differences due to manufacturing tolerances are generally insignificant. Thus, $Z_1 = Z_2$, and the following equation is true when considering lines of the same type

$$a_N = \ln\frac{U_1}{U_2} \text{ in Np resp.} = 20\lg\frac{U_1}{U_2} \text{ in dB}.$$

It is obvious, from Fig. 29, that the near-end cross-talk attenuation unit is

$$a_N = \ln\frac{U_{10}}{U_{20}} \text{ in Np resp.} = 20\lg\frac{U_{10}}{U_{20}} \text{ in dB}.$$

And the far-end cross-talk attenuation unit is

$$a_f = \ln\frac{U_{10}}{U_{21}} \text{ in Np resp.} = 20\lg\frac{U_{10}}{U_{21}} \text{ in dB}.$$

For metering reasons it is advisable to measure the voltages, (U_{11}) on the line causing the interference, and (U_{21}) on the line subject to the interference, at the far end. When taking account of the fact that the ratio U_{10}/U_{11} represents the total

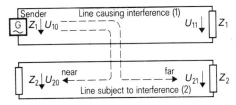

Fig. 29   Cross-talk

attenuation of the line causing the interference, the far-end cross-talk attenuation unit can also be expressed as follows:

$$a_f = \ln \frac{U_{11}}{U_{21}} + \ln \frac{U_{10}}{U_{11}} = \ln \frac{U_{11}}{U_{21}} + a \text{ in Np}$$

or,

$$a_f - a = \ln \frac{U_{11}}{U_{21}} \text{ in Np}.$$

The expression $a_f - a$ is known as the basic value in the far-end cross-talk attenuation unit.

According to the CCITT recommendations the basic value in the far-end and near-end cross-talk attenuation between two telephone circuits, right up to the terminal exchanges, should be not less than 58 dB (6.7 Np) for terminal traffic on international and connected national AF cable lines. The value to be allotted (for example, to exchange installations) is included in this.

The basic value in the far-end and near-end cross-talk attenuation between two different, but similarly designed, two-wire circuits should be at least 61 dB (7 Np) for the repeater sections, on loaded internationally connected AF cable lines.

As the quality of the transmission lines increases, the minimum value of the near-end cross-talk attenuation has to be increased. Thus the line constant in the far-end cross-talk attenuation between symmetrical two-wire lines for CF cables, which carry 12 two-wire systems, must be at least 70 dB (8.0 Np) for each repeater section, provided that the lines are terminated by their characteristic impedance.

When designing telecommunications cable installations in view of the required cross-talk attenuation, account has to be taken of the fact that different types of lines or transmission directions may be contained in a single cable, since the requirements regarding cross-talk between any two lines will differ if there are differences in the line attenuation, or the transmitter level, and also if a single line is extended or if a single line in a cable has been removed or through connected.

Attention must also be paid to the fact that, at times, each of the single lines can behave as a line causing interference or as a line subject to interference.

Nor should the fact be overlooked that, in CF lines, the cross-talk in some of the channels can be intelligible whilst on others it may be unintelligible (see 6.2.3.).

These remarks will show how carefully the possible instances of cross-talk must be investigated when dealing with combined communications cables to calculate the most critical conditions for each type of cross-talk.

6.4.1. Cross-talk between symmetrical lines – couplings

Linear, or intelligible, cross-talk between two symmetrical lines is caused by coupling.

A distinction must be made between

(a) *capacitative coupling* (capacitance unbalance) which is attributable to dissymmetrics in the electrical field caused by deviations in the dielectric make-up of the cable and

(b) *magnetic coupling* produced by dissymmetrics in the geometrical structure of the cable.

In AF cables the effect of magnetic coupling on cross-talk is generally small compared with the effect of capacitative coupling. The effects of magnetic coupling only become noticeable eventually if the capacitive couplings have been severely reduced by cross-talk compensation;

(c) *galvanic coupling*, normally due to differences in resistance. The interference effect of such couplings is made noticeable in the so-called phenomenon of side-to-phantom cross-talk i.e., when phantom circuits are in use.

The following symbols are commonly used to represent the capacitative and magnetic couplings of symmetrical cables.

Cross-talk in quads	Capacitative Coupling	Magnetic Coupling
Cross-talk from side circuit 1 to side circuit 2	k_1	m_1
Side-to-phantom cross-talk from side circuit 1 to phantom circuit	k_2	m_2
Side-to-phantom cross-talk from side circuit 2 to phantom circuit	k_3	m_3
Side-to-side cross-talk between different quads		
from phantom I to phantom II	k_4	m_4
from side circuit I_1 to phantom II	k_5	m_5
from side circuit I_2 to phantom II	k_6	m_6
from phantom I to side circuit II_1	k_7	m_7
from phantom I to side circuit II_2	k_8	m_8
from side circuit I_1 to side circuit $_1$	k_9	m_9
from side circuit I_1 to side circuit II_2	k_{10}	m_{10}
from side circuit I_2 to side circuit II_1	k_{11}	m_{11}
from side circuit I_2 to side circuit II_2	k_{12}	m_{12}

In the instance of k_1, for example, the cross-talk which occurs in both directions, i.e., from "side circuit I to side circuit II" and from "side circuit II to side circuit I" is of the same value.

The symbols I and II indicate the quad resp. neighbouring quad, whilst 1 and 2 indicate the side circuits in the quads.

A further distinction is made between:

Couplings to earth

side circuit 1 to earth and screen or metal sheath e_1
side circuit 2 to earth and screen or metal sheath e_2
phantom to earth and screen or metal sheath e_3

Couplings external to earth

side circuit 1 to earth and screen or metal sheath e_{a1}
side circuit 2 to earth and screen or metal sheath e_{a2}
phantom to earth and screen or metal sheath e_{a3}

In a paired-cable pair, due to dissymmetries in the two wires, there is only the *earth coupling e*. In a star quad, however, there are six so-called "*internal quad couplings*" ($k_{1,2,3}$ and $e_{1,2,3}$). Fig. 30 shows a star quad with its partial capacitances between the four wires and between earth and the four wires.

The cross-talk between the two side circuits $(1-2$ and $3-4)$ within a star quad (side-to-side cross-talk) is caused by the k_1 coupling which is:

$$k_1 = (C_{13} + C_{24}) - (C_{14} + C_{23}).$$

This shows that k_1 is the residual capacitance, between the two side circuits, caused by unavoidable manufacturing tolerances.

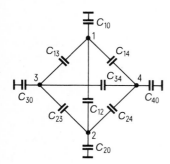

Fig. 30
A star quad with its
partial capacitances

The cross-talk between a side circuit and a phantom circuit (side-to-phantom cross-talk) is caused by the k_2, k_3 couplings.

$$k_2 = (C_{13} + C_{14}) - (C_{23} + C_{24}) + \frac{C_{10} - C_{20}}{2}$$

$$k_3 = (C_{13} + C_{23}) - (C_{14} + C_{24}) + \frac{C_{30} - C_{40}}{2}.$$

Maximum values for the k_2, k_3 couplings, which may not be exceeded, must be guaranteed for all AF star quad cables using phantom circuits. CF star quads, although they do not use phantom circuits, must fulfil very strict requirements regarding the k_2, k_3 couplings, because they can produce "*third-circuit couplings*" between the side circuits via the phantom circuit.

Additional, internal quad couplings are the couplings to earth (e_a, e) which can cause interference in the lines (e_a, power current influence), or of cross-talk via a third circuit (e; in this instance, the earth-return circuit).

The couplings $e_1, e_2 (e_{a1}, e_{a2})$ refer to the two side circuits in a star quad, and are defined as

$$e_1 \triangleq (e_{a1}) = C_{10} - C_{20}$$
$$e_2 \triangleq (e_{a2}) = C_{30} - C_{40}.$$

The e_3- (e_{a3}-) coupling refers to the phantom circuit in a star quad and is

$$e_3 \triangleq (e_{a3}) = (C_{10} + C_{20}) - (C_{30} + C_{40}).$$

There are various causes for these couplings. k_1-couplings occur when the twist of the quads is very short (considerable deformation of the wire), and when it is very long (unstable quad). k_1 couplings are also caused, for example, by variations in the resultant dielectric constant, by faults of the quads caused during the stranding process, and by the inaccurate geometrical structure of the quad.

In addition to the causes already mentioned, $k_{2,3}$-couplings are caused by variations in the thickness of the wires, of the conductors etc. The causes, for $e_{1,2}$-couplings, excepting for the faults in the star quads during the stranding process, are the same as for $k_{1\ldots3}$ couplings. The origin of e_3-couplings is in the arrangement of the four wires in a star quad: if, for example they form the four corners of a rhombus, instead of the four corners of a square.

The magnetic couplings are produced by the mutual inductance between the lines. The magnetic linkage between two lines is at a minimum when the conducting loops are geometrically perpendicular to one another. This is ideally the case for the two side circuits of a star quad (m_1). Generally, the magnetic couplings are proportional to the capacitive couplings.

The capacitative couplings $k_{4\ldots12}$ and magnetic couplings $m_{4\ldots12}$ *(side-to-side cross-talk couplings)* are couplings which occur between the symmetrical elements of the stranding.

When the stranding elements are stranded close together, the term *adjacent coupling* is used of two, adjacent, stranded elements. If there are different strands *(separating elements)* between two stranded elements alongside one another in the stranding, then it is a problem of *couplings between non-adjacent strands.*

Any relationships between strands arranged in different layers of strands are known as *inter-layer couplings.*

The mutual couplings between different stranded elements are dependent on the ratios of the effective twist given to each stranded element.

When a cable core is stranded without any return-twisting, the mutual position of the stranded elements is not altered by the twisting of the layer; this means that the amount of twist (which is the determinative factor for decoupling) is the same as the amount of twist given to the individual elements in the strand.

There is a disadvantage in twisting the layers without permitting any return-twisting; the separate elements in a strand are turned through $360°$ for each length of layer twist. This disadvantage is avoided by permitting a certain amount of return-twisting when stranding the layers. In such an instance the separate elements in the strand suffer no additional torsional stress. The relative position of the individual elements changes, if return twisting is permitted when the layers are stranded, as if each element in the strand, after each length of layer twist, had made one complete turn in opposition to the direction of twist of the stranded layer.

Cross-talk attenuation in individual (factory) cable lengths

The following equation, which is generally true for the cross-talk attenuation, namely,

$$a_N = \ln \frac{U_1}{U_2} + \frac{1}{2} \ln \frac{Z_2}{Z_1} \text{ in Np resp.} = 20 \lg \frac{U_1}{U_2} + 10 \lg \frac{Z_2}{Z_1} \text{ in dB}$$

can be transformed for electrically-short sections, and then gives the following approximation for

capacitive couplings:

$$a_N = \ln \frac{2}{\omega \cdot k \cdot Z_m} \text{ in Np resp.} = 20 \lg \frac{2}{\omega \cdot k \cdot Z_m} \text{ in dB}$$

magnetic couplings:

$$a_N = \ln \frac{2 \cdot Z_m}{\omega \cdot m} \text{ in Np resp.} = 20 \lg \frac{2 \cdot Z_m}{\omega \cdot m} \text{ in dB .}$$

144

The following coupling values have to be substituted for k, m and Z_m.

$$k = \frac{1}{4} k_{1,4\dots12} \quad \text{or} \quad \frac{1}{2} k_{2,3}$$

$$m = m_{1\dots12}$$

$$Z_\mathrm{m} = \sqrt{Z_1 \cdot Z_2} \,;$$

where $Z_1 = Z_2$ then $Z_\mathrm{m} = Z_1 = Z_2$.

For k and m couplings the measured value, converted where necessary to the reference length, must be used: hence the equation for k_1-couplings becomes

$$a_\mathrm{N} = \ln \frac{8}{\omega \cdot k_1 \cdot Z_\mathrm{m}} \text{ in Np resp.} = 20 \lg \frac{8}{\omega \cdot k_1 \cdot Z_\mathrm{m}} \text{ in dB} .$$

Cross-talk attenuation on sections which are not electrically short

When the separate stranding elements are connected together in a logically sequential numerical order, i.e., when making a *direct connection* of separate elements, the couplings (which differ entirely from length to length) of the different elements make up a *total coupling*. In such instances it is therefore of importance whether the couplings are systematic, i.e., whether they are produced by some regularly-occurring effect, or whether they are unsystematic, i.e., produced by a number of various, random, causes with varying mutual effects.

Pure *systematic couplings* have the same sign ($+$ or $-$), and approximately the same value over the whole length of a production batch. The resultant total coupling consequently increases in proportion to the number of lengths connected together.

Unsystematic couplings vary from stranding element to stranding element, and from length to length, in both sign and value. Since it is impossible to make any exact statement regarding the distribution of the unsystematic couplings, an average value is obtained from the single values for the couplings. In electrically short sections, these couplings increase in proportion to the square root of the length, $\sqrt{\dfrac{l}{l_0}}$ (where l_0 is the reference length).

When telecommunications-cables are carefully manufactured the fraction due to systematic coupling is slight, so that without serious error the increase in the mean coupling values for the stranding elements can be considered to be proportional to $\sqrt{\dfrac{l}{l_0}}$.

Loading coil section

In accordance with the relationship $\sqrt{\dfrac{l}{l_0}}$, the mean near-end and far-end cross-talk attenuation in the instance of direct connections of n lengths will decrease by an amount

$$\Delta a_N = \frac{1}{2} \ln n \text{ in Np resp.} = 10 \lg n \text{ in dB} .$$

If, for example, there are four factory lengths in the loading section, the total coupling in the side-circuit line of a star quad, over the loading section, is $\sqrt{4} = 2$ times greater than the coupling of the individual length. With direct connections the cross-talk attenuation is thus reduced by

$$\Delta a_N = \frac{1}{2} \ln 4 \approx 0.7 \text{ Np resp.} = 10 \lg 4 \approx 6 \text{ dB} .$$

Line section

Near-end cross-talk

With direct interconnections containing an even greater number n of similar lengths, and with approximately the same average value for the couplings, the increase in the total coupling is no longer proportional to $\sqrt{\dfrac{l}{l_0}}$ but gradually gets less until it finally reaches a constant value. In the instance of near-end cross-talk this is explained by the fact that the energy flowing over the route, consisting of the transmitter, the line causing the interference, the line subject to the interference, and the receiver, is attenuated, depending on the distance of each partial coupling from the transmitter/receiver in proportion to the line loss. Therefore, the fraction effectively due to near-end cross-talk decreases with the increase in the distance of the partial couplings from the transmitter. Where lines have no relay amplifiers the lowest value for the near-end cross-talk attenuation will be, approximately, obtained when the line-loss constant, working from the transmitter, has a value $a = \alpha \cdot l$ of approximately 22 dB (2.5 Np). The connection of further lengths causes no reduction in the value of the near-end cross-talk attenuation.

Far-end cross-talk

In contrast to near-end cross-talk, and for far-end cross-talk where n equal lengths are interconnected in a direct connection, the path for the energy flowing across the (partial) couplings is always equally long. Depending on the local position of the partial coupling, the energy first spreads (for a lesser or greater distance) along the line causing the interference and covers the remainder of the route along the line subject to the interference. The partial couplings for n lengths thus increase in practically the same way as the far-end cross-talk.

Example of the various ways of crossing lines to balance out k_1 couplings.
(e.g. line L_1: $k_1 = +25\,\mathrm{pF}$, line L_2: $k_1 = -65\,\mathrm{pF}$).

Crossing within side circuit

Position	side circuit		Effect

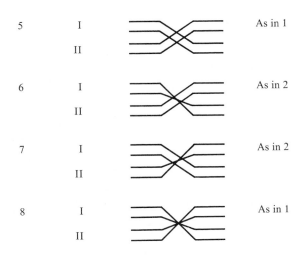

Position	side circuit	Effect
1	I	The interconnection of the couplings depends on the signs $(+25) + (-65) = -40\,\mathrm{pF}$
	II	
2	I	The second length changes the sign $(+25) + (+65) = +90\,\mathrm{pF}$
	II	
3	I	As in 2 (for side circuit II)
	II	
4	I	As in 1
	II	

Crossing with change of position and crossing of side circuits

5	I	As in 1
	II	
6	I	As in 2
	II	
7	I	As in 2
	II	
8	I	As in 1
	II	

Fig. 31   Balancing of couplings by crossing

This can be expressed in another way by saying that, in any direct interconnection of n equal lengths the far-end cross-talk attenuation decreases by the amount Δa_N. Reflected near-end cross-talk, however, also contributes to the far-end cross-talk, and for this reason the number and value of differences in characteristic impedance must be kept as small as possible.

Cross-talk balancing

In contrast with the direct connections of n equal lengths, the values for cross-talk attenuation can be substantially improved if the joints for the side circuits at specified cable length connection points are made by interchanging (crossing) the wires instead of connecting them in numerical order.

The crossing of the lines is performed either within the side circuits of a quad, by interchanging the two wires, or by interchanging the two side circuit lines in a quad (by change of position). In this latter instance both the wires in the side circuits may also be interchanged. Fig. 31 illustrates this in greater detail.

Frequently, however, since the crossing of the wires does not provide sufficient compensation, it is necessary to increase the cross-talk attenuation by incorporating compensating units. Even in these instances, an attempt is made to improve the cross-talk attenuation by *pre-crossing*, so that only the residual compensation has to be undertaken by the compensating units. These units are capacitors which are incorporated as near as possible to the point of concentration of the couplings between the wires affected, and to a considerable extent balance out the couplings in concentrated form. In rare instances, complex compensating units are required (R–C combinations) especially if it is a matter of third circuit couplings.

6.4.2. Cross-talk between coaxial lines

In symmetrical lines, the line subject to interference is affected, predominantly, with the capacitative and magnetic coupling by the line causing the interference. In coaxial cables, however, cross-talk is due to other causes.

In coaxial lines (coaxial pair) the problem is predominantly that of galvanic coupling since the disturbing effect is due to the coupling resistance of the external conductor. In a coaxial pair, due to the screening arrangement of the external conductor, the total electro-magnetic field is contained inside the line.

The coupling resistance of a coaxial pair is defined as:

$$R_k = U_I/I \; ;$$

where R_k is the coupling resistance in Ω;

U_I is the open-circuit voltage which appears in the coaxial circuit as a result of the interference current;

I is the interference current closed outside of the coaxial pair.

In a closed, metal tube the coupling resistance decreases sharply as the frequency increases, due to the skin effect. Normal designs for the external conductors of coaxial cables, however, consist of metal tapes, or half shells formed into tubes. The electro-magnetic field thus penetrates the air gap which is now present, so that the coupling resistance above a certain frequency again increases.

As regards its interference effects, the value of the coupling resistance is not dependent solely on the frequency but is also affected by the design of the external conductor, and by the conditions in the neighbourhood of the coaxial pair, i.e., it is dependent on the total arrangement of the communications cable.

Cross-talk between coaxial pairs in a cable can be reduced by increasing the inductance of the loops formed by the external conductors of the coaxial pairs. This is achieved by spinning high-permeability steel tapes externally round the coaxial pair. It is usual to have two layers of steel tape. Besides increasing the inductance, the steel tape also covers the air gap in the external copper conductor, and largely suppresses the increase in the coupling resistance.

By reason of the design of the coaxial pair, and the arrangement of the cable, it is impossible to make any further improvement in the cross-talk attenuation of the manufactured length on an actual section of the line, such as is possible with symmetrical cables.

7. Telecommunications cable installations – interference effects and protective measures

7.1. Communications installations

Communications installations can be divided into three classes: A, B and C.

Class A comprises those installations with but simple claims on the transmission reliability, such as, for example, bell and house/domestic telephone systems.

Class B installations must have higher transmission reliability; although they include telegraph, remote control, and telephone installations as well as warning equipment (danger or emergency), they nevertheless do not require quite such high standards of reliability as do Class C installations.

As for class B installations, those in Class C must also satisfy high standards of reliability, but these are furthermore improved by additional measures. As regards their construction and installation the line, repair and service systems are of a much higher order, whilst every possible technical precaution is taken to avoid failures. Included in this class are fire and burglary alarms emergency systems and railway signalling installations.

Any room or location equipped with electrical equipment is termed an *operating point*. As regards accessibility, a distinction must be made between:

- public operating points, accessible to anyone;

- operating points with limited accessibility (usually only accessible to authorised personnel) such as, for example, selector and amplifier stations and those telephone installations where the components subjected to voltage during operation must be protected against accidental contact;

- closed operating points, kept under lock and key which are only accessible to authorised staff under express instructions, such as cable distribution stations, unmanned relay-amplifier stations, high voltage telephone installations, switching and distribution installations and equipments in locked locations.

The design, installation and maintenance of communications installations must ensure that, by their faultless operation, no one shall be endangered and that no material damage can occur.

Beyond this further precautions must be taken in view of faults.

Power circuits and communications circuits must be electrically separated from one another.

The conductors for telecommunications circuits may only be included in the cabling for those lines which provide the power supplies for telecommunications installations, provided that the following precautions are taken;

- the groups of lines must be separated by a conducting screen having a cross-section which satisfies the specifications for protective conductors, and forms an integral part of the protection of the power supply system

- the two groups of lines must have additional or increased insulation. When the power circuit is operating with a voltage of 250 V against earth, the total insulation between the two groups of lines must withstand an alternating test voltage twice the voltage value of the communications circuit but not less than 2.5 kV. In case of alternating voltage the r.m.s. value is valid.

Communications lines may also be used for the simultaneous transmission of electrical power (remote power supplies) provided that attention has been paid to the specifications for the installation of remote power supply installations (VDE[1] 0800 Part 3).

The communications lines of different communications installations (or of different classes) may only be contained within the same cable if there are satisfactory precautions against going over the voltage, and if neighbouring circuits are only affecting themselves within the permissible limits.

No special precautions are taken to prevent accidental contact with components of a communications system, while they are subjected to the operating voltage, provided that such components are everywhere sufficiently insulated (operating insulation) and provided that

- in open operating points the voltages which occur, with respect to earth, are not greater than 65 V a.c. or 100 V d.c.

- these voltages in limited accessible or closed operating points are not more than 250 V with respect to earth.

The a.c. voltages quoted above are r.m.s. values.

Additional precautions against excessive contact voltages in communications installations, or in component parts which are not associated with power supplies are only required if

- there is a possibility of a.c. voltages, greater than 65 V w.r.t. earth or d.c. voltages, greater than 100 V w.r.t. earth, likely to endanger life.

- there is danger to domestic animals through the appearances of a.c. voltages greater than 24 V with respect to earth.

In both the above instances the a.c. voltages are r.m.s. values.

---

[1] Verein deutscher Elektrotechniker (German Association of Electrical Engineers).

7.2. Interference effects in communications installations

7.2.1. Exposure to danger

Any threat of endangering the human body through the possible effects of electrical currents must be avoided. As a rule, the phenomena consequent upon such accidents are due to the passage of the current through the body. In such instances the actual resistance, whether from hand to foot or from hand to hand, is of critical importance. The following, can be considered as the average values to be expected:

$500\,\Omega$ for the internal bodily resistance
$1000\,\Omega$ as the lower limits if a hand is damp
$3000\,\Omega$ as an average value for the total resistance.

Alternating current is generally more dangerous than direct current.

An immediate danger of death only exists with a.c. currents higher than 80 mA.

The a.c. voltage of 65 V mentioned in 7.1. is calculated approximately as

$$U_\sim = I \cdot R = 20\,\text{mA} \cdot 3000\,\Omega = 60\,\text{V} \sim.$$

The necessary safety margin is thus obvious. The only voltages, however, which are considered to be free from danger, are those less than or equal to 42 V.

Even under normal operating conditions, dangerous voltages can be induced, in communications cables, laid in the ground, from high tension installations operated with lack of symmetry w.r.t. earth such as, for example, single-phase a.c. railways. The same thing can happen on self-supporting overhead communications cables arranged on the same pylons as three-phase high-tension lines and also with underground cables laid closely adjacent to these.

In most cases dangerous voltages are, however, induced in communications cables from three-phase high-tension lines when there is a short-circuit to earth since, under the normal operating conditions for a high-tension line, the magnetic field in the three phases cancel one another.

Critical voltage limits are also dependent on the type of communications cable and on the condition of the power line. Table 7 gives limiting values for the critical voltages.

7.2.2. Disturbing effects

As regards *disturbing effects* on communications cables, a distinction is made between functional disturbances in the signal circuits and *noise* voltages in the audio circuits.

152

Functional disturbances such as, for example, faulty dialling, faulty counting and faulty trips, can be caused by extraneous voltages. On telephone connections, which use an earth return, interference may occur if, for example, the induced EMF E_{iN} during normal operation of $16\frac{2}{3}$ Hz a.c. railway lines is greater than 10 V or greater than 20 V on 50 Hz a.c. railway lines. These values are valid for telephone installations operating on 60 V d.c. operating voltage. The corresponding values for 24 V are 4 V and 8 V.

Depending on the sensitivy of the listener's ear, and the transmission characteristic of the telephone receiver the noise voltages are dependent upon frequency.

Due to the large number of harmonics caused by a.c. rectification or thyristor control devices affected communications cables have exceptionally high noise voltages. Under normal operating conditions interference effects are seldom to be expected from three-phase installations.

The noise EMF produced by inductive, capacitative, and ohmic effects must not exceed the following limiting values at the terminal point (subscriber).

On telephone lines for public traffic (DBP) and on international connections of the German Federal Railways (DB)   1 mV

On telephone lines of non-public traffic

> Line circuits in cables   5 mV
>
> The desirable value is   2 mV
>
> Telephone open wire lines, inclusive short line circuits in cables connected to these open wire lines, as well as line circuits in overhead cables   10 mV
>
> The desirable value is   5 mV
>
> Line circuits which can be connected to the telephone lines of the German Federal Telephone System (DBP), or to international connections of the DB   1 mV

7.2.3. The causes of voltage-surges

Voltage surges in communications installations are caused by external electrical effects such as, for instance, atmospheric effects, or through the effects of power-supply installations.

These voltage surges may be produced by:

(a) the effects of lightning, either by its striking the communications cable directly or by the flash-over as a result of an earthed part of the installation being directly hit. Electrical interference in communications cables is often due either to the effects of lightning between clouds or to a single stroke of lightning in the vicinity of the cable when very high voltage-surges may occur.

Table 7   Limiting values for voltages dangerous to life

Type of communications line		Normally-operated single-phase railway or three-phase resp. single-phase-high-tension overhead lines	Dangerous short-circuit to earth, either from a railway overhead line or from a three-phase high-tension overhead line		(Additional) Protective measures
			At a shut-down time ≤ 0.5 s		
Without a transformer termination	Open wire line Cable	$E_{iN} \leq 65$ V		$E_{iK} \leq 500$ V^1	Not necessary
	Open wire line Cable	$E_{iN} > 65$ V		$E_{iK} > 500$ V^1	Necessary; Indicated additionally by the electrical danger arrow
With a transformer termination	Open wire line	$65\ V < E_{iN} \leq 125$ V	Short-time interference	—	Not necessary, Indicated additionally by the electrical danger arrow
	Cable	$65\ V < E_{iN} \leq 250$ V		$500\ V^1 < E_{iK} \leq 1200\ V^2$	
	Open wire line	$E_{iN} > 125$ V		$E_{iK} > 500$ V^1	Necessary; Indicated additionally by the electrical danger arrow
	Cable	$E_{iN} > 250$ V	—	$E_{iK} > 1200\ V^2$	

E_{iN} voltage between communications wires and earth when high-voltage line is operating normally.

E_{iK} voltage between communications wires and earth when there exists a short-circuit on the high-voltage line.

1. For installations on the DBP 300 V (instead of 500 V) corresponds to the 430 V recommended by the CCITT, when considering an expecting-factor $w = 0.7$ ($w = 1$ corresponds to the calculation for the short-circuit current under most unfavourable circumstances which are unlikely to happen).

2. 1200 V = 60% of the usual test voltage for communications cables (here, 2000 V) between wire and metal sheath or screen.

(b) neighbouring power-supply installations. Tables 1 and 2 in VDE 0228/4.65 show the instances in which precautions must be taken against such effects. According to the Table, power cables and power-supply networks without a rigidly-earthed neutral (usually less than 110 V) are not critical. In such instances their effect only need be checked if the quenching voltage for the residual current in the short-circuit to earth is exceeded. In networks rated up to 30 kV the permissible residual current, according to VDE 0228/4.65 Fig. 2 is $\leqq 60\,A$.

(c) Charging of the conductor by the electric field. Open wire lines, with great differences in altitude or just before storms, are the most likely to be affected. Cables without an earthed metal covering (screen) suffer from capacitance effects just like open wire lines.

7.2.4. Measures to prevent voltage-surges in communication cables

Precautionary measures

Only the most important precautionary measures will be mentioned here.

When laying overhead lines or unscreened cables every advantage should be taken of the protection provided by the terrain to avoid or reduce any capacitive charging; for instance, making use of clefts in the terrain.

Unsymmetrical operation (the use of an earth-return circuit) should be avoided. Communications cables, moreover, should have good longitudinal symmetry, and should be properly balanced to ground (i.e., uniform, low, couplings to earth).

The selection of the most suitable line is very important. The separation between communications cables and d.c. railway lines (rectifiers) should, in towns where possible be greater than 100 m, in open country greater than 500 m, whilst the separation between communications cables and a.c. railway lines resp. high-voltage lines should, in towns, be greater than 250 m, and in open country greater than 1000 m. With trunk cables, the separation from high-tension lines in towns should be greater than 500 m, and greater than 2000 m in open country, to avoid any excessively high interference with communications cables.

Where it is clear that communications cables are liable to be affected, the use of cable with a suitably-low reduction factor becomes necessary (e.g., with an aluminium sheath and armouring with steel tape. The reduction factor will, however, only be effective if the metal sheathing of the cable, and any available armouring are properly earthed, not merely at the ends of the cable sections but also, so far as possible, at all cable-introducing points.

Occasionally, it is advisable to use cable of greater electric strength either wire/wire (by thickening the insulation covering of the conductors) or wire/earth (by thickening the cable core wrapping or by arranging an internal plastic sheath under the cable screening or its metal sheath).

155

Danger-limiting measures

A distinction must be made between inductive or ohmic interference and those due to capacitive charges.

The following precautions can be taken to limit the voltages which may occur as the result of inductive or ohmic effects.

(a) connecting *surge-voltage-arrestors* to the communication-cable conductors. This is an effective precaution against the occurrence of transient voltage-surges. In such instances the arrestors only respond if the critical voltage is greater than the response voltage of the arrestor. These arrestors are connected either to the beginning and end of the section of the line likely to be affected, or at the subsequent, i.e., next, cable outlets (e.g., terminal heads and disconnecting strips).

Where an open wire communications line is connected to a cable, the latter must be protected against all the possible voltage-surges on the open wire line. This is achieved by surge-arrestors. Because of the most essential matching of the differing characteristic impedances of the two kinds of lines, matching transformers are additionally provided.

(b) incorporating transformers at the terminal points of the lines of communications cables likely to be affected, resp. at the subsequent, i.e., next cable outlets (e.g., terminal heads and disconnecting strips).

To ensure that the permissible interference voltage is not exceeded, it is sometimes necessary to separate those lines likely to be affected with isolating transformers. In such instances it must be remembered that the *separating transformers* will not transmit d.c., and that they cause an additional attenuation.

On any communications cable the protective measures taken should be of the same type, or should be mutually adjusted. Fitting some of the cable lines with voltage arrestors, whilst leaving the remaining lines in the same cable without arrestors (or terminating then with transformers) is a practice to be carefully avoided, since this would cause impermissibly-high voltage differences due to the effects of the dissymmetry thus produced between the lines or groups of lines within the cable.

Where the lines of an unscreened trunk cable are capacitively charged, such devices as suppression coils should be used where the charging current between the line and earth exceeds about 9 mA.

7.2.5. Interference to communication lines in cables

Three types of interference are shown (from left to right) in Fig. 32

inductive	$(\omega \cdot M;$	electro-magnetic field)
ohmic	$(R;$	increase of potential)
capacitive	$(\omega \cdot C;$	electric field)

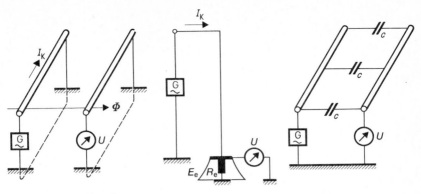

Fig. 32 Types of interference

Generally, it is only the inductive and ohmic interferences that are important, because communications cables are usually screened and thus are unaffected by capacitive interference.

As regards interference it is practical to consider the interference effects of power supplies and lightning, separately.

Power line interference

If a high power-supply installation is earth-connected, excessively-high voltages may appear in the lines of the communications cable if it happens to be laid parallel to, but at an insufficient distance from, the high-tension overhead lines or cables, or if it is brought into a power station or transformer station and if it is insufficiently screened. Such voltages may cause disturbances in communication lines, may endanger the communications installations, and may even endanger human life.

When discussing disturbances due to power supplies, a distinction must be made between ohmic and inductive coupling between the power supply and communications installations.

Ohmic coupling

If a high-tension overhead line is short-circuited to earth the potential, I_K, at the earthing resistor, R_e, of a power station or transformer station, will rise (with respect to earth at the other end) – caused by the earth-short-circuit current, I_K, – by an amount

$$E_e = I_K \cdot R_e.$$

Any communications cable introduced into the power station will be affected by this voltage in the earth circuit.

157

The effect of this voltage on the lines in the communications cable is lessened by the reducing effect of the metal sheath, if at least at both ends of the cable the metal sheath is earthed.

Thus the ohmic (galvanic) induced voltage in the circuit between the wire of the communications cable and its sheath becomes

$$E_g = I_K \cdot R_e \cdot r_u \; ;$$

where E_g is the interference voltage, in V, due to the galvanic effect; I_K is the short-circuit current to earth in A; R_e is the earth resistance of the earth at the plant in Ohm; r_u is the reduction factor of the communications cable.

The reduction factors of any other cables or conductors connected to the power station earth may be neglected, since their effect is included in the earthing resistance R_e.

Full advantage of the reducing effect of the protection given to long-distance communications cables by steel tapes, cannot be taken because of the saturation of the steel tape when large currents flow in the sheathing.

If, however, the communications cable has been laid insulated (e.g., with an external protective covering of plastic material) within "voltage funnel" and, possibly, beyond this, then a steel tape armouring of the cable, if its metal sheath is connected to the power station earth, can have a reducing effect. Earthing the sheathing and if possible the armouring of the cable at its ends (and, in certain instances, at intermediate points) is, of course, absolutely essential.

Inductive coupling

When an overhead high-tension line is short-circuited to earth, the short-circuit current I_K induces by its magnetic field a voltage in the communications cable laid parallel to it. The value of this voltage is a function of I_K, the frequency of the interfering installation, the mutual inductance M, the length l of the distance where the line is in parallel, and the total reduction factor, r.

$$E_i = \omega M \cdot l \cdot I_K \cdot r$$

where E_i is the induced interference voltage, in V; ω is the angular frequency, in $\dfrac{1}{s}$; M is the mutual inductance between the line causing the interference and the line subjected to the interference, in $\dfrac{mH}{km}$. The mutual inductance is a function of the actual distance between the parallel lines, the conductivity of the ground $\left(\text{e.g., clay soil, is approx. } 10^{-4}\,\dfrac{S}{cm} \right)$, and the frequency of the line causing the

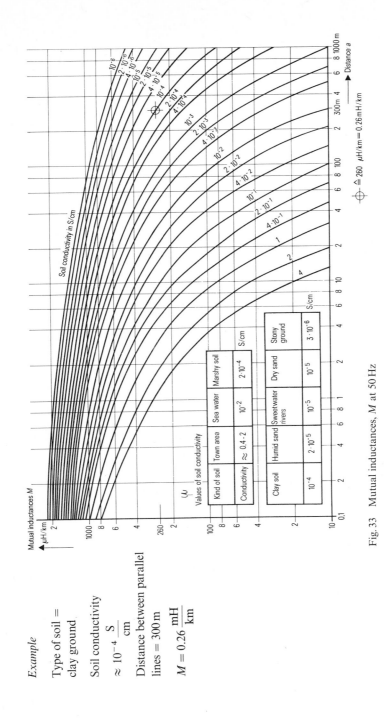

Example

Type of soil = clay ground

Soil conductivity ≈ $10^{-4}\ \dfrac{\text{S}}{\text{cm}}$

Distance between parallel lines = 300 m

$M = 0.26\ \dfrac{\text{mH}}{\text{km}}$

Fig. 33 Mutual inductances, M at 50 Hz

159

interference. Values for the size of M, at the frequency of 50 Hz, can be obtained from the graphs in Fig. 33; l (in km) is the length of the parallel runs of the overhead high-tension line and the communication cable; I_K is the short-circuit current to earth; where high voltage networks have a rigidly-earthed neutral, even a simple connection to earth may cause interference. Networks earthed via a choke, or with an insulated neutral only become critical if two phases are simultaneously earthed at different places (double short-circuit to earth).

As regards interference in communications cables, a value three times the zero current, $3 I_0$, must be inserted for the high-tension line as the short-circuit current to earth. In general, when calculating the interference voltage E_i, it is necessary to take into account the maximum possible short-circuit current to earth at the point on the parallel section of the overhead high-tension line and the communications cable, which is furthest from the power station or transformer station (short-circuit point). More precise details are given in VDE 0102 and 0228.

r is the product of the reduction factors

$$\text{e.g., } r = r_i \cdot r_s \cdot r_e \cdot r_k \cdot r_u$$

where r_i is the reduction factor of a power cable (with overhead high-tension lines, or overhead electric railway supplies this is not required); r_s is the reduction factor of the railway lines; when the rails are connected together with a good-quality conductor, $r_s \approx 0.5$; with poor-conductivity rail joints (generally, on unelectrified railways) $r_s \approx 0.8$; r_e is the reduction factor of the earth wire, which is a function of its cross-section and material (conductivity): e.g., for 70 mm² steel, $r_e \approx 0.98$; for 70 mm² bronze, $r_e \approx 0.7$; for "stalu" with a 200 mm² aluminium portion, $r_e \approx 0.65$; r_k is the reduction factor of a compensating conductor (an additional earthed conductor, laid along the line, subject to interference, such as, for example, a water pipe). r_u is the reduction factor of the communications cable.

The reduction factor of a communications cable is defined as

$$r_u = \frac{\substack{\text{longitudinal (series) EMF,} \\ \text{conductor to earth in the presence of a metal envelope}}}{\substack{\text{longitudinal (series) EMF,} \\ \text{conductor to earth without a metal envelope}}} .$$

The reduction factor r_u is thus a measure of the screening effect of the metal envelope on a cable; i.e., a measure of the extent to which it protects the communications lines in the cable from inductive or resistive interference effects.

Metal envelopes of a cable are the metal sheath or metal screen including the metal wires which may be stranded directly above or below the screen and which are in constant conducting connection with the screen.

The reduction effect of a metal envelope on a communications cable can be explained as follows.

When there is a short-circuit to earth, the high-tension line forms a closed circuit in conjunction with the earth. The short-circuit current, I_k, flowing to earth in this circuit produces an electromagnetic field Φ_1 which develops a specified voltage E in a second circuit consisting of, for example, an insulated conductor (without any metal envelope) and the earth. If any metal envelope is arranged round this conductor then it behaves as a *short-circuit winding*, if it forms a closed circuit with the earth. A current I then flows in this short-circuit winding, in the opposite direction to the short-circuit current I_k. The current I produces an opposing electro-magnetic field Φ_2 which reduces the field Φ_1 (which induces the voltage E), with the result that a correspondingly smaller voltage E_i appears in the circuit between the conductor and earth.

If resistance R of the metal envelope is decreased, the current I and the strength of the opposing field Φ_2 also increase whilst the voltage E_i between the conductor and earth reduces. The effect of the short-circuit winding between the metal envelope and earth is expressed by the reduction factor.

$$r_u = \frac{E_i}{E}$$

which can be calculated from the resistance of the metal envelope and the inductance of the ground circuit (metal envelope/earth).

For the normal range of frequencies ($16^2/_3$ and 50 Hz), and for the range of speech frequencies, the reduction factor for, say, a communications cable with a metal envelope (but without any steel tape armouring) can be calculated as follows:

$$r_u = \frac{R}{\sqrt{R^2 + \omega^2 L_e^2}}$$

where R is the d.c. resistance of the earthed metal evelope on the cable in $\dfrac{\text{ohms}}{\text{km}}$

$\omega = 2\pi f$ is the angular frequency in $\dfrac{1}{\text{s}}$; L_e is the inductance of the ground circuit metal envelope to earth which is approximately $2\dfrac{\text{mH}}{\text{km}}$.

If the earthing resistance is unaltered, resistance R decreases in proportion as the specific resistance ϱ of the metal envelope is reduced. For this reason it is better to use communications cabling with an aluminium sheath, rather than a lead sheath, in any region affected by interference from high voltages.

Where cables have an external envelope or sheath made of plastic material, the metal sheath or screen is insulated from earth, with the result that the metal envelope must at least be earthed at the ends of the cable section. In such an instance it is necessary to substitute, for the resistance R (in ohms) in the previous formula

$$R = \frac{R' \cdot l + 2 \cdot R_e}{l} \, ;$$

where R' is the d.c. resistance of the cable or screen in ohms/km; R_e is the earthing resistance per each end of the cable in ohms; l is the distance between the earthing points in km.

Full advantage of the effect of the reduction factor, r_u, of a communication cable can only be gained if the sum of the transition resistances (earthing resistances) is small in comparison with the d.c. resistance of the cable sheathing and the armour (or screen) on the length of cable subject to interference. This condition is satisfied, for long lengths of *well-earthed cable*, i.e., a cable in continuous contact with the earth, with a metal sheathing (e.g., without any plastic covering).

Throughout the whole range of electric field strengths (in V/km), the reduction factor r_u of unarmoured cable is constant. Tape or circular-section wire armouring proportionally improves the electrical conductivity of the cable sheathing.

A steel tape armouring (with overlapped layers) can essentially improve the reduction factor r_u by its magnetic effects. The most satisfactory value for the reduction factor is obtained at a frequency of 50 Hz for electrical field strengths in the range 100 to 300 V/km (optimal magnetisation of the steel tapes).

If further admittance is provided such as, for example, by flat wire-armouring on top of the steel tape, then the most satisfactory (lowest value) for the reduction factor, r_u, is obtained with somewhat higher electric field strengths.

With armoured aluminium sheathed cables the lowest reduction factors can be obtained in an economical way.

Inductive and ohmic coupling

Where a communications cable, which has been taken into a power station or transformer station, then runs parallel with the outgoing high-tension overhead line, the total voltage interference can be calculated as follows:

$$E_{ig} = \sqrt{E_i^2 + E_g^2}$$

where E_{ig} is the total voltage interference in V.

Effects of lightning

Overhead cables, introduction cables into buildings, and points of transition from cable laid in the ground to overhead cable or open wire lines, are particularly subject to the danger of being struck by lightning.

Where the lightning discharge is powerful enough, even ground-laid cable can be damaged if the sheathing is not satisfactory. Communications cables, when lightning occurs, may be damaged or even destroyed by reason of the heating and pressure effects (the pressure effect being due to the explosive manner in which the moisture evaporates, particularly with coaxial cable), and as a result of the high voltages which appear between the cable conductor and earth (ohmic and/or inductive coupling). Moreover, precautions have to be taken against the resultant voltages at the accessible ends of the cable sector which could endanger life as well as equipment.

In areas subject to the dangers of lightning the design and installation of the cable system must, consequently, ensure robust mechanical strength. In addition, the electrical strength between the cable conductors and the metal sheathing or screen must be high, whilst the external armouring of the cable (without any extra protective envelope, i.e. cable make-up for direct contact with the earth) must have good conducting properties to enable the lightning current to be rapidly drained away.

At every cable jointing sleeve the metal sheathing (screen) and the armouring must have longitudinal and transverse interconnections (the cross-section of the stranded copper wire must be at least 16 mm^2).

Where cables are likely to be endangered by lightning they must be connected to voltage arrestors at the ends of a cable section or at the points where cables are brought out so as to protect both the equipment and maintenance staff. For that purpose all the conductors of the communications cable must be earthed via the arrestors.

The metal sheathing (screen), the armouring, and, for *overhead cable*, the supporting wire must be directly connected to all the earth points provided (e.g., the earth points for the masts and those for the lightning protectors).

With light-weight aerial cables *(figure-eight cables)* the supporting wire must – if possible – be earthed at each mast, the screen is only earthed directly at the ends of the section, provided there are voltage arrestors fitted between the conductors and earth.

There exist the following possible methods of protecting a cable

- increasing the electrical strength between the cable conductor and the metal sheathing (screen) by thickening the cable core wrapping, or applying an internal sheath of plastic material. The test voltage between conductor and metal sheathing must be at least 4 kV r.m.s.
- by applying a heavily-galvanised round or flat wire armouring, without any external protective covering, to provide insulation with respect to earth (e.g., no protective covering of plastic material) so that the armouring is in contact with the earth
- producing the cable-sheath from a good conducting metal such as aluminium.

For unarmoured communications cables covered with plastic sheaths, particularly the precautions against damage or electrical interference are substantially improved by laying one or two tapes of galvanised iron in parallel with the cable in the cable run.

Such steel tapes have proved to be of especial advantage where the cable runs are laid in rising ground (e.g., hill-tops). They must, however, be of sufficient length, i.e., they must extend into an area where the ground is a good conductor. Special precautions must, therefore be taken if the cable requiring protection is laid in dry or rocky ground. When such cables (e.g., armoured but without any external plastic sheath, or unarmoured) are laid in contact with the earth, no copper, whether in strips, stranded wire or wire, should be used, since the resulting voltaic action may cause the electrolytic disintegration of the cable materials.

Effects of interference due to radio transmitters

High-power, long and medium wave, transmitters can cause interference in CF transmission lines where the cable run is in the vicinity ($<$ about 1 km) of such transmitters.

7.3. Earthing equipment of telecommunications installations

The leakage of dangerous or disturbing currents into the earth is one of the essential tasks of earthing equipments. They should also provide protection against excessive interference or contact voltages. From the point of view of transmission engineering they are used as a part of the operating circuit, since they also provide, inter alia, definite reference voltages for metering purposes.

Where an *earth point* is required *for a communications system* it must be connected to an earthing equipment with essential low earthing resistance.

The metal sheaths of cable laid in contact with the ground, and even water pipes, should be used as earths.

Gas pipes should never be used as earth-points for communications systems since the separate lengths of piping are insulated, with, e.g., hemp, at their joints.

It is general practice to connect to an earthing device the following metal components or equipments; frequently, an earthing installation is formed partially by these metal components or equipments:

as earth points:

any metal sheathing on communications cables which is in conducting contact with the earth;

164

any available earth, in particular piping, metal strips, or steel;

a lightning-protector installation, if it is available, for a building (its actual earth with no water pipes);

eventually water pipes;

for earthing:

the metal sheathing on communications cables with an insulating protective cover;

water, gas and heating pipes, as well as fastening clamps for voltage balancing devices;

the neutral conductor in a low-voltage network protected by a no-volt device.

The total resistance of the operating earth in a communications system is usually between about 0.5 to 10 ohms.

Generally, in practice, it is desirable to make the values for the earth points as low as possible. This is especially true of communications cables likely to suffer interference from power supplies or lightning.

Special rules have to be adopted for the earthing devices of communications cables in underground railway installations. The *railway earth* (the rails) cannot be used for communications cabling i.e., it is absolutely essential to separate the earthing mechanism for the communications cabling, including the communications system, from the rails.

In such instances the communications cable, should, where possible, be connected to an external earth (water-earth). This requirements can only be easily satisfied in above-ground stations. In underground stations the external earth has to be insulated and brought through the brickwork into the operating room. The expense of such a method is, however, scarcely justifiable. Consequently, the most usual structure is the so-called potential rail which is interconnected, at the separating planes in the concrete structure, with copper stranded rope.

To ensure that the potential rail is isolated from the railway earth the terminal racks in which the communications cables are introduced are erected in an insulated manner, or else the cable sheath resp. screen is interrupted in front of the rack (Railway engineering method). In this latter instance the various components arranged in the rack e.g., isolating strips, terminal connectors and transformers, must be insulated before their incorporation in the rack. The earth rail, also insulated before its incorporation in the rack, is then connected, via insulated terminal connectors, either to the potential rail or to the cable sheathing or screen. The conducting connection so formed then acts as the earthing point for the associated communications equipment.

There are occasions where underground railway systems also operate partially above ground. If the underground installations are connected to a potential rail, and if the above ground installations are connected to an external earth, then the metal sheathing or screen of the communications cable must be isolated at the transition points with an insulating sleeve.

8. Design of systems and equipment

8.1. Design of telephone systems

8.1.1. Method of telephone supplies – local battery and central battery operation

Local batteries

When using *local battery supplies* every telephone set has its own battery, which is connected to the microphone circuit. The operating supply is of the order of only a few volts. The inter-connecting line carries no d.c. current, only the *a.c. audio current* induced by the microphone circuit in the interconnecting line and the *a.c. calling current* (Fig. 34). With local battery supplies there are thus no supply-current losses.

Simple, portable *telephones equipped with local batteries* such as, for instance, field service telephones, are for the most part equipped with a *manually-operated magneto generator*. The a.c. calling current thus inductively induced in the two-wire inter-connection is transmitted to the station at the other end, where it initiates the *calling signal* e.g. an alarm.

Because of the a.c. calling current the operational range of telephone equipment supplies from local batteries is large in comparison with equipment supplies from central batteries. Telephone equipment supplied from local batteries is thus particularly suitable for use on long AF lines without relay amplifiers – for example coil-loaded *two-wire service lines.*

On very long lines fed via local batteries, use is made of modern portable local-battery-supplied equipment *(service line telephones)* which contain, in one common housing, both an AF amplifier and a universal *matching transformer.* By this means a line attenuation of some 52 dB (6 Np) can be compensated at a frequency of 1200 Hz. It is thus possible, depending on the diameter of the conductor, to telephone via loaded two-wire lines over distances up to several 100 km.

Such local-battery-supplied installations are generally not fitted with *selector dialling equipment.* Consequently, all the other telephone sets connected to the local battery-fed connecting line receive the calling signal released by the caller. Because those

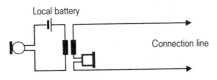

Fig. 34   Local battery supplies

who have not been directly called can listen in to the conversation, such divices are unsuitable for public or similar telephone services.

Selector dialling equipment on company lines can, in the broadest sense, be considered as a local-battery-supplied telephone system insofar as it is true that the supplies to these telephone installations with selector dialling equipment are locally provided.

The selector dialling equipments, for automatic selector dialling between all the subscribers connected to a company line, are *telephone service equipment for plants*. They are used to make for example telephone connections along oil-lines and product-lines (pipe lines), for water- and electricity supply undertakings, for railway-, road- and inland shipping-administrations and for metallurgical works.

The required connection is automatically produced by the selection of a number, i.e., no exchange is required. With selector dialling the selected telephone is the only equipment which receives a calling signal. No other subscriber can join in any conversation that is taking place.

Generally, only one conversation can take place at any one time on a private company line. Much greater advantage can be gained from such lines, however, when they are divided into several sections by connecting *coupling transformers* into the line. Communications can thus be made along each of the separate sectors, but it is also possible, besides making a connection between neighbouring sectors, to make a connection with an exchange via a special number.

Selector dialling installations use selector processes by which the signals are transmitted without any d.c. components. Consequently, all the equipments in such an installation can be disconnected galvanicly from the line, d.c.-wise, by transformers, with the result that interference-free operation is possible even in the neighbourhood of high power installations (e.g., high-tension overhead lines, and electrified railways).

The W11 selector dialling equipment is used on AF two-wire lines. The *calling range* of the inductively-produced selector pulses is several hundred kilometres, depending on the diameter of the conductors in the interconnecting line and on the type of line transformer. As the number of subscriber connections increases, however, the reduction range is, on average, a little steeper than directly proportional. The total reference equivalent between the two remotest subscribers, however, determines the *audio range* of these selector dialling installations. Because of the fact that such equipments are generally used in rooms where the noise level is higher than 60 phons, the total reference equivalent should not exceed 22 dB (2.5 Np). In exceptional instances, greater values of total reference equivalent are permissible, but the value of 36 dB (4.2 Np) must never be exceeded. Where the total reference equivalent is 22 dB (2.5 Np) it is possible with *trunk line transformers* to cover a range of approximately 40 km on unloaded lines, where the diameter of the conductors (copper) is 0.9 mm, and to cover approximately 90 km on loaded lines with conductors having the same diameter (0.9 mm) and 80 mH coil inductance spaced 1700 m apart. It is generally impossible to use relay amplifiers to increase the audio range since the *balancing networks* at the *four-wire terminations* of the AF two-wire amplifier, cannot be sufficiently accurately adjusted due to the number of telephones connected in parallel to the private company line.

In contrast with W11 selector dialling installations which give audio ranges of about 100 km, much greater ranges (up to 1000 km) depending upon the *transmission path*, can be achieved with W12 installations. Because *identical frequency two-wire AF systems* are unsuitable for such long ranges, the transmission systems used are either *four-wire identical frequency systems* or *two-wire separate frequency systems*. Four-wire lines with AF amplifiers, or CF-systems operated with four-wires (e.g., V60 and V120) are of the former type, whilst CF-systems operated on two wires are of the latter type (e.g., Z12, Z24). To avoid cross-talk interference, so far as is possible, on AF four-wire lines both side-circuit lines (pairs) in the same star quad should not be used. The method of transmitting the selector signals on the trunk line depends on the type of transmission system. AF four-wire lines use *voice frequency selecting system* (e.g., at a frequency of 2280 Hz). CF-systems with an *in-band selecting system* transmit the selector signals within the audio band (frequency range, 300 to 3400 Hz). Where CF-systems have out-of-band selector dialling systems (channel selection) the selector signals are supplied as d.c. signals. CF-installations then convert these signals into the usual selector signals appropriate to the actual system, and deliver them once again to the station at the other end of the line as d.c. signals.

Central battery supplies

With a *central-battery supply* system the microphones at all the telephone stations are fed from a common battery. The central battery (with a voltage of 24, 48 or 60 V) which is centrally located, for example, in the local exchange, is connected to the local subscriber's line via *feed-coils* or *feed-relays* which limit the voltage to the permissible operating voltage for the microphone. The a.c. audio current is inductively transmitted to the earphone circuit. During speech, the a.c. audio current, which flows in the subscriber's line, is superimposed on the direct current.

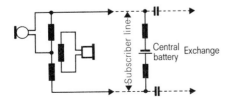

Fig. 35   Central battery supply

When using a central battery supply the attenuation in the subscriber's line is increased by the supply-current losses which occur between the central battery and the microphone (e.g., 4 dB per 1000 ohm loop-resistance with a 60 V d.c. central battery supply).

Central battery ring supply

With a *ring supply* a common battery is also used. The separate telephone stations are, however, arranged in the same way as for local battery circuits with the result that the only current flowing in the subscriber's line is the a.c. audio current, inductively induced from the microphone. The isolated central battery ringline is connected to the microphone circuit via feed-coils. A capacitor connected across the microphone-circuit shunts the resistance of the feed-coils for the current fluctuations produced by the microphone.

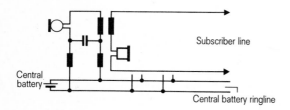

Subscriber line

Central battery

Central battery ringline

Fig. 36
Central battery ring supply

8.1.2. Selector dialling systems for local and trunk exchanges

Local exchanges

In addition to the permissible reference equivalent, the operational range also has to be taken into consideration when designing and installing local exchanges.

The operational range is dependent upon the type of selector system, the supply voltage and such supply current losses as occur. In the exchange installations that have been customary so far *(stepping selectors, noble-metal uniselector motor-switches)*, the operational limit at which the transmission of the selector pulses can be assured is a loop resistance of some 1250 Ω on the subscriber's line, where the supply voltage is 60 V d.c.

With new selector systems it will be possible to extend the operational range to a loop resistance of some 1800 Ω.

In the engineering of local exchanges, since the only available current sources in the subscriber network are d.c., the usual switching signals, which unambiguously define the making and breaking of the connection in both directions, are transmitted

170

as d.c. signals via the speech wires and, if necessary, via the signal wires (c-wire in exchange). The signals can be transmitted as pulsed or continuous signals.

A great variety of *relay repeaters* are used in exchange to convert and transmit various switching signals, and also to effect other switching tasks. Only those essentially relevant to the subject will be briefly explained here.

Thus, for example, it is possible for several different telephone selector systems to be operated simultaneously by means of *matching relay repeaters.*

If, as a result of the excessive length of the line and, consequently, the unduly-high loop resistance, the operational range is exceeded, a *range relay repeater* is then added (in the local exchange) to the incoming subscriber's line, or in a connection between two local exchanges. In such an instance the currents from the incoming switching signals will be too weak, or will be distorted, with the result that the relays will no longer operate correctly. The relay circuit in the range relay repeater, however, responds reliably to the reduced currents and, via contacts, operates other circuits suitable for normal current conditions.

The following is another method of ensuring the proper transmission of signals, in the local exchange, where there are groups of excessively-long subscriber lines. In this method a part of the exchange is located in the neighbourhood of the telephone station. This *partial local exchange* is equipped with *pulse relay repeaters* which take over some of the functions of the *complete exchange* (local exchange), including the supply to the microphones in the telephone equipment and the transmission of the selector dialling tone. The *loop interruption pulses* which come from the subscriber's dial are converted into current pulses and fed to the main exchange.

If the *extension dialling system* is connected to a public exchange *relay repeaters* are required in addition to the normal exchange facilities. They can be used both for uni-directional audio traffic, whether outward or inward, and simultaneous bi-directional audio traffic.

Trunk exchanges

Depending upon the type of line and transmission system, the switching signals and the number dialling pulses can be transmitted, at *trunk exchange technique*, along the trunk lines by direct current, by induced pulses, by alternating current at audio frequencies or at frequencies beyond the normal audio-frequency band *(CF-channel selection)*.

The trunk lines are connected to the exchange installations via *toll selecting relay repeaters.* Such repeaters are, on principle, located in the selector installation.

The purpose of a toll selecting relay repeater, besides the transmission of the audio-frequency band, is to convert the d.c. switching signals from the selector device into signals appropriate to the actual toll selecting method, and to transmit these to the trunk lines. Conversely, the toll selecting signals from the trunk line are re-shaped by the toll selecting relay repeaters into selecting signals appropriate to the dialling device, and conveyed to the exchange installations.

Suitable toll switching transformers are provided for the different types of toll switching process.

D.C. Relay repeater

Within telephone exchanges three wires are generally needed to make the connection. Two wires (the "a" and "b" wires) are required for audio transmission. The third wire (the "c" wire) performs various switching processes while the connection is being made.

Where it is necessary to connect together, for example, the selector stages of two exchanges sited 10 km apart, this method is most uneconomic since the communications cable must then contain 50% more wires. To reduce the wire requirement, *d.c. relay repeaters* are included in the lines leaving the exchanges. The function of these relay repeaters is to transfer the switching functions of the "c" wire to one or both of the wires ("a" or "b" wire) in the audio circuit.

The switching signals are transmitted as d.c. pulses (d.c. selection). The pulse required to release the "c" wire in the exchange at the end of a conversation is produced, in the older equipments, via a transformer in the transmitter section of the relay repeater.

This pulse lights a glow lamp in the receiver portion of the relay repeater at the other end and which thus causes a relay, connected to the "c" wire, to de-energize. More recent devices make use of an *a.c. release*. An a.c. pulse is transmitted at a frequency of 25 or 50 Hz, and releases the "c" wire in the receiver of the exchange at the other end. The a.c. release provides a more reliable type of transmission.

The range of d.c. pulses is limited. For copper conductors, 0.8 mm diameter, the maximum range is 35 km but can be extended to approximately 45 km if the conductor diameter is increased to 0.9 mm. But, to ensure reliable dialling, it is not generally usual to take full advantage of these maximum values.

When operating with d.c. currents the interconnecting lines cannot be wired to transformers. Moreover, the lines are in direct galvanic electrical connection with all the ancillary equipment. D.C. selection is, therefore, unsuitable for communications equipments likely to be affected by power supply installations.

Inductive selector relay repeater

To improve the transmission properties of communication lines they are connected at the ends, i.e., at the junctions to the exchange equipment, to transformers. The selector arrangements are thus generally protected against interference from external voltages. D.C. current pulses cannot, of course, be used as switching signals since the lines are no longer continuous. The transmitted and received pulses must therefore be conveyed, to the connecting line or from it to the exchange at the other end, inductively by transformers.

One possible method is to convert the d.c. pulses from the selector device, in the exchange, into current pulses or peaks which at the receiver end, are reshaped into d.c. pulses. This is the purpose of *inductive selector relay repeaters*.

Inductive selector dialling is also suitable for communications cable installations likely to suffer interference from power supplies and is, for example, usually employed with the W11 selector dialling installation for private company lines.

A.C. Selector relay repeaters

With a.c. selector systems the switching signals transmitted are a.c. pulses. For this purpose a signal generator at the exchange produces a.c. currents at frequencies of 25 Hz, 50 Hz and, sometimes, 100 Hz or 150 Hz which are formed into suitable pulses by the *a.c. selector relay repeater* and supplied to the trunk line. The relatively, weak a.c. pulses arriving at the other end are reconverted into the d.c. pulses normally required by the selector mechanism at the exchange.

A.C. selection, with a signal transmission frequency of 25 Hz, is used for counting during an outgoing conversation and is located between the *local exchange* and repeater centre. With a transmitter voltage of, for example, 30 V a.c., and 0.9 mm diameter conductors the range is approximately 150 km.

Using a.c. selection at 50 Hz the range for 0.9 mm copper conductors for example, is also about 150 km.

Because normal AF amplifiers will not transmit such low frequencies – this also applies to d.c. selection and to the current peaks with inductive selection – the relay amplifiers have to be equipped with *call-diverting switches*.

In-band signalling relay repeater

To avoid the additional expense of diverting switches, when transmitting a.c. pulses etc. as switching signals on AF trunk lines with relay amplifiers, the switching signals can also be sent within the audio-frequency band. This method is known as *audio frequency selection* and also as *in-band signalling*, and is usually operated at a selection frequency of 3000 Hz. For *single frequency selection* a frequency of 2280 Hz is also common. There is also the *dual frequency method* at frequencies of 2040 and 2400 Hz. Any undesired signal transmission via the audio transmission system is prevented by means of *audio-suppression devices* or by special signals.

The selection frequency, produced by an *AF signal generator*, is transformed by a relay repeater into the appropriate pulses and is then transmitted to the trunk line.

The range of audio frequency selection is similar to that of the transmission system in use.

With long trunk lines which are, on principle, loaded, intermediate relay amplifiers must be provided in addition to the terminal amplifiers. In such instances, in addition to the intermediate relay amplifiers, four-wire terminations with balancing networks are also required. With increasing number of intermediate relay amplifiers, these terminations cause a deterioration in the electrical stability of the line. As a result of possible feed-back there may be "whistling" on the transmission line. For this reason, AF trunk lines requiring a large number of intermediate relay amplifiers are operated with four wires instead of two. Due to possible differences in levels and, consequently, to possible differences in cross-talk the two line circuits needed for the two transmission directions shall not belong to the same quad in the communications cable.

Carrier frequency selection (Channel selection)

The carrier frequency technique facilitates multiple the use of a single line. By this method several or a plurality of multiples of AF bands (300 to 3400 Hz) are superimposed on the *carrier frequency*. The dialling signals, or switching signals, for each group are transmitted in special frequency channels outside the corresponding audio frequency band. The (dialling) *signal frequencies* commonly used for this purpose are 3825 or 3850 Hz.

Since the selector frequencies in use lie within the frequency spacing between two carrier frequencies (4 kHz raster) and, therefore, lie within the carrier frequency channel, the expression *channel selection* or *out-of-band signalling* is used. Since it is only used with carrier frequency systems, channel selection is also often known as carrier frequency selection.

In this system the d.c. signals from the selector mechanism on the transmitter are connected via a *trunk selecting relay repeater* to the signalling circuits in the terminal equipment of the carrier frequency system, which then feed the signal frequency into the CF-channel. The opposite process takes place at the receiver end.

Because the signal is separated, frequency-wise, from audio signal, the switching signals cannot be affected by the audio frequencies.

The range of any carrier-frequency dialling system is the same as the range of the carrier frequency system.

8.2. AF and CF Transmission systems

Any audio transmission along wires requires a channel for each of the audio directions (two-way audio communication or duplex operation). These channels can be

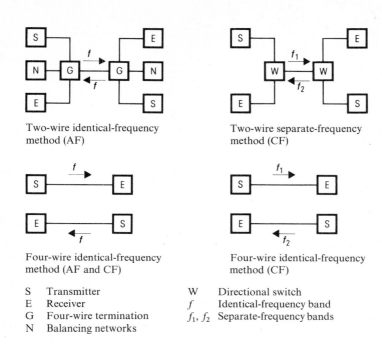

Two-wire identical-frequency
method (AF)

Two-wire separate-frequency
method (CF)

Four-wire identical-frequency
method (AF and CF)

Four-wire identical-frequency
method (CF)

S   Transmitter   W   Directional switch
E   Receiver f Identical-frequency band
G   Four-wire termination f_1, f_2 Separate-frequency bands
N   Balancing networks

Fig. 37   Methods of transmission for duplex operation

designed for two-wire operation (a common line for the outward and return directions) to operate on the same or on separate frequency bands. With four-wire
operation one line is necessary for each direction, and these are normally operated
in the same frequency band.

8.2.1. AF Transmission systems

The simplest type of AF transmission is two-wire operation (identical-frequency
method) via AF lines which are not loaded and have no amplifiers[1]. This method
is extensively used in local networks, in trunk extension networks, in the public trunk
system, in small networks or in the connections of private intercommunication
systems and in subscriber's extensions. Four-wire terminations are not required on
lines that contain no amplifiers. The ends of the lines are either connected directly
to the telephone equipment (e.g., local battery operation without selector dialling)
or via trunk selector relay repeaters to the exchange equipment.

To prevent excessive attenuation distortion, unloaded lines should not have a line
attenuation greater than 8.7 dB (1 Np) at a frequency of 800 Hz, in case they may

---

[1]) amplifier = repeater.

175

not be subjected to other limits as regards permissible reference equivalent, or as regards the operating range of the calling or selector dialling devices. Loading of the lines can be of some assistance where the line attenuation values are fairly high.

The use of transistorised negative-line resistance (NLT) amplifiers is another way of reducing the attenuation of unloaded two-wire lines. This amplifier is fitted, for example, in the connecting line between the extension and the local exchange in the public telephone system. At a frequency of 800 Hz at the line termination the maximum amplification is some 7 dB (0.8 Np). NLT amplifiers will transmit low-frequency alternating currents, direct currents and the 16 kHz charge meter pulses in both directions. The d.c. is used for calling and selector dialling.

When the lines are loaded the upper utilizable frequency depends on the type of line (mutual capacity, side-circuit or phantom operation, method of stranding) and on the method of loading (coil inductance and coil spacing), and is between 2 to 3.4 kHz. If the coil spacing is kept constant any increase in the value of the coil inductances lowers the upper frequency limit. On the other hand, there is a much greater reduction in the line attenuation than when using coils of lower inductances.

Within the effective-frequency band there is little attenuation distortion on loaded, two-wire, AF lines operated without amplifiers. The permissible value for boundary distortions of 8.7 dB (1 Np) (according to the recommendations of CCITT) in a total connection, where the loaded line has a loading section of 1.7 km and a coil inductance of 80 mH, will not be exceeded when the length of the line is shorter than about 250 km. On the basis of a main line with 0.9 mm diameter conductors which, if loaded as already detailed, has an attenuation constant of approximately 0.22 dB/km (25 mNp/km), then a line of 250 km would have a line attenuation of 54 dB (6.25 Np). This would thus be greatly in excess of the value of 36 dB recommended by CCITT for the total reference equivalent on un-amplified AF lines, and this value of 36 dB in addition to the line attenuation, includes the sending reference equivalent in the microphone, the supply current attenuation, the loss within the exchange, and the receiving reference equivalent in the earphone.

If the total reference equivalent is not greater than 22 dB (2.5 Np) and in exceptional instances such as, for example, service lines, if it is not greater than 36 dB (4.2 Np), loaded, AF, two-wire lines are generally operated without amplifiers. For higher attenuations, loaded lines are equipped with terminal, and sometimes with intermediate, amplifiers.

Four-wire terminations with line-balancing networks are required when using AF amplifiers on two-wire lines, because of the identical frequency method. Since one separate amplifier must always be used for audio in one, single, direction, it is the purpose of the four-wire termination to convert the two audio directions in the two-wire line circuit into a "four-wire circuit" where each direction of transmission can have its own associated amplifier. Since the balancing networks with the four-wire terminations cannot be ideally matched to the two-wire line, the stability of the transmission line deteriorates as the number of intermediate amplifiers is increased. To avoid whistling, resulting from feedback in the two-wire line, it is not useful to eliminate attenuation by means of AF amplifiers. There is thus a limiting range for two-wire lines operating with amplifiers.

The range of lines with AF amplifiers can be considerably extended if a fourwire, instead of a two-wire, connection is provided. In this way it is possible to extend distances to more than 1000 km. Two separate line circuits are supplied for the two transmission routes (the outward and return lines). By reason of the cross-talk attenuation which is necessarily increased as a result of the difference in levels, these circuits are formed from two-wire transmission circuits belonging to different quads within the communications cable. Such a transmission is known as a *four-wire identical-frequency system*. Four-wire terminations are only required at the terminations of the four-wire circuit. They are not required for each of the intermediate amplifiers.

Thus problems of stability are avoided; therefore the four-wire line can be (theoretically) designed to be entirely without attenuation.

Universal amplifiers are commonly used as AF amplifiers since they can be used universally both as regards the required matching to the different types of line and their bandwidths, and also as regards their amplification and their distortion elimination. They can be used as terminal amplifiers on a two-wire line with a two-wire or four-wire connection to the exchange, as two-wire intermediate amplifier, as four-wire terminal amplifier with two-wire or four-wire connection to the exchange, or as four-wire intermediate amplifiers. A universal amplifier contains two amplifiers, distortion eliminators, and balancing circuits for the two different directions of transmission. The a.c., at a frequency of 16 to 50 Hz, for calling and selector dialling is made to by-pass the universal amplifier by means of a *call* or *selector dialling by-pass circuit*.

8.2.2. CF Transmission systems

All types of long-distance communications traffic make use of carrier-frequency techniques. This is due to the increasing application of multiple utilisation techniques to line circuits, particularly to coaxial pairs. In comparison with AF techniques this has caused a substantial reduction in capital expenditure per audio circuit. This applies both to the cable costs and to the costs of the relay amplifiers. Indeed, a further satisfactory reduction has been achieved by the introduction of transistors. For long-distance traffic AF techniques have, therefore, only a limited application and are reserved for long lines, with only a few audio channels, or for short lines with a large number of audio channels. As an approximation it is generally true to say that CF techniques are more economic than AF methods for long lines with more than six audio circuits, and for lines with a large number of pairs which are more than 20 to 25 km long.

The development of CF systems is in accordance with the recommendations of CCITT. Accordingly, the AF channels in which the bandwidth covers the range 300 to 3400 Hz are converted into the CF position in the 4 kHz raster. The carrier frequency supply to a CF system is based on a multiple of 4 kHz. The audio-frequency band is supplied to the AF input of the channel modulator which, nowadays, is fully-transistorised. The d.c. switching signals from the exchange are converted in a signal unit to the signal frequencies of 3825 Hz or 3850 Hz, and then connected to the CF channel.

The channels 1, 2, 3 or 4, 5, 6 etc. are modulated in channel modulators by means of the channel carrier-frequencies which originate in the carrier-frequency supply. These frequencies, of 12, 16 and 20 kHz, can be allotted to anyone of the three channels. During the modulation process the lower sidebands are filtered out. The three channels form a *pregroup* with a breadth of 12 kHz in the frequency positions 60 to 72, 72 to 84, 84 to 96 or 96 to 108 kHz.

In *primary-group amplifiers* the four pregroups (consisting of 12 channels) are combined into, and amplified as, a *primary group* (in the frequency range 60 to 108 kHz).

By modulation with five further carrier-frequencies, five primary groups in the frequency band 60 to 108 kHz are converted in the *primary group converter* into a *basic supergroup* in the frequency band 312 to 552 kHz, and therefore, containing 60 channels.

From five supergroups a *basic tertiary group* can be formed with 300 channels in the frequency band 812 to 2044 kHz, and from three tertiary, or from 15 supergroups, a *basic quarternary group* with 900 channels can be formed (in the frequency band 8516 to 12388 kHz).

Thus, depending upon the CF system, there are a series of *interconnection levels* which facilitate simple and inexpensive branch-circuit techniques without any need to make conversions to the AF levels. Instead of one audio-frequency band (300 to 3400 Hz), each channel can from basic principles, be supplied with a maximum of 24 (WT) *a.c. telegraphy channels* or can be operated as a *video telegraph transmission line* or a *long-distance data transmission line.*

The varying number of intermediate repeaters (section equipment) that are required – besides the amplifiers and converters at the terminal positions – depends upon the type of CF system in use, on the components in the communications cable and on the length of the connection. These intermediate amplifiers can be housed in buildings and supplied locally, or can be fed from a remote supply. The intermediate amplifiers designed to be housed in relatively small containers beneath floors, which require practically no maintenance, are most frequently fed from a remote supply.

The necessary d.c. supplies for the section equipment, which today are all fitted with semiconductors (transistors) are transmitted below the CF-currents which carry the information along the line circuits (remote power supply). *Series supply*, via the internal conductor of coaxial pairs, is a very economic method of supplying the intermediate amplifiers on coaxial lines. The remote power supply equipment, installed at the amplifier station feeding the power, supplies a current, depending on the CF system, of some 40 to 90 mA, which flows in succession through all the remotely-supplied intermediate amplifiers.

By means of resistors the d.c. voltage on the internal conductor of the coaxial pair is high-resistance-balanced relative to the external conductor. The value of the voltage depends on the type of CF system, and on the number of remotely-supplied amplifiers. It varies between $\pm 300\,V$ to $\pm 600\,V$.

If the intermediate amplifiers are fed from a d.c. series supply, where the internal conductor is one continuous unearthed connection over the complete remote supply line, then the external conductor of the coaxial pair is never directly earthed but is connected to the remote supply equipment (floating potential) via a very high resistance (usually 1 MΩ). If the communications cable is then subjected to interference from power supplies, the voltage effects on the coaxial pair are substantially less than they would be if the external conductor were directly earthed.

When using two-wire lines, CF systems are operated by the *separate-frequency process*. When using four-wire lines the *identical-frequency process* is the most usual.

Two-wire separate-frequency process

In the *two-wire separate-frequency process* the same pair of conductors ("a" and "b" wires) are used for both transmission directions. Two frequency bands, in different positions in the frequency spectrum, are used for the two directions.

The best-known system of this type is the Z12 (12 channels) CF system with a 6 to 108 kHz frequency band. The 6 to 54 kHz band is available for transmission from A to B and the 60 to 108 kHz band is available for transmission from B to A, in the opposite direction. The transmission lines, which are not loaded, most commonly make use of communications cable containing paper- or polythene (PE)-insulated copper conductors 0.9 or 1.4 mm diameter. With such cables the repeater sections can be respectively some 24 or 35 km. Use is also made, however, of conductors 0.8, 1.2 or 1.3 mm diameter.

Four-wire identical-frequency process

One line is necessary for each direction of transmission. Both directions use the same frequency band. Since this produces conditions for the attenuation of near- end cross-talk, which cannot be fulfilled if such a CF system uses cables with symmetrical stranded items, CF systems for symmetrical cables (V60, V120), consequently, have a separate unloaded line circuit for each of the out-going and return directions, laid in two separate cables. In the instance of CF systems for coaxial cables (V300, V960, V1260, V2700, V10 800), the coaxial pairs for both directions can, however, be laid within the same cable since, by reason of their design coaxial cables have much more satisfactory cross-talk characteristics.

Of the systems for symmetrical lines the CF system V60 (60 channels), now only rarely used, is operated in the 12 to 252 kHz frequency band with paper-insulated conductors of 1.2 diameter, the average repeater section being 18 km. In the V120 system (120 channels) the CF cables have conductors, 1.3 mm diameter, insulated with styroflex. The frequency band is between 12 and 552 kHz, and the standard repeater section is also 18 km.

The 1.2/4.4 mm coaxial pairs (small diameter coaxial pairs) are predominantly reserved for the V300 system (300 channels in the 60 to 1300 kHz transmission band, with approximately 8 km repeater sections) and for the V960 system (960 channels in the 60 to 4028 kHz transmission band, with repeater sections of approximately 4 km).

2.6/9.5 mm coaxial pairs (standard coaxial pairs) are used in the CF systems, V960 (which has repeater sections of some 9 km), V1260 (1260 channels in the 60 to 5516 kHz transmission band with repeater sections of some 9 km), V2700 (2700 channels in the 312 to 12 388 kHz transmission band with repeater sections of some 4.5 km and, recently, also in the V10 800 system (10 800 channels in the 3 to 59 MHz transmission band with repeater sections approximately 1.5 km).

8.3. Telephone installations for electric power-supply companies

In addition to the public telephone system operated by the Postal and Telegraph Authorities there are quite a number of telephone installations run by private and official institutions, the telephone systems of the power-supply undertaking (ESU) being amongst the most important of these. According to the respective requirements, directions regarding the control or distribution of electrical power can be transmitted over these telephone systems.

ESU communications installations are, where so authorised, private communications systems where the exchanges generally are connected to private branch exchanges which on their part are connected to the public telephone network. The connection between the two installations is made by a *communications switchboard*. This is thus both the answering position and exchange for the private telephone system, and the answering position for the private branch exchange. The communications circuit also enables the operating staff to obtain connections in either direction, and to make manual exchange calls. Coupling between the ESU and public telephone systems, besides being forbidden by law, is impossible.

Single exchanges separated by very great distances are sometimes connected together by different transmission systems.

The main network of ESU installations consists of several interconnected groups of networks. *Net group dialling switches* with *pulse repeaters* ensure that the proper connections are made, that alternative routes will be arranged if the direct line is engaged, and contribute to ensuring that there is a continuous flow of information, through proper use of the transmission routes.

Each group of networks consists of several junction installation (JI) areas. The associated *terminal installations* (TI) are star connected to the *junction installations* which are, for the most part, interconnected. In addition to the terminal installation, the terminal installation area includes the subordinate installations (SI) i.e., the telephone units connected to it.

The junction installations contain the exchange equipment for the selector dialling traffic, whilst the terminal installations contain the exchange equipment for the terminal traffic and the internal traffic between the telephones belonging to one terminal installation.

There is a difference in transmission between simple connections made by a ringing call, and connections made by selector dialling. The first types terminate at the communications switchboard and are then transmitted by a manually-operated exchange. The associated telephone equipment which can be fed either from local or central batteries, can generally be dialled and is operated on the AF two-wire principle.

Connections made by selector dialling are trunk lines which are connected to the exchange installations, and are also directly connected to the communications switchboard. They make use of either the two-wire or the four-wire process. AF, CF and power-line carriers (PLC – carrier frequency transmission via power lines) or directional radio links, can be used as the transmitting circuits.

The Association of German Electric Power Stations has produced an attenuation plan for the communications networks of ESUs. This plan, which, in principle, is practically the same as that of the German Federal Posts and Telegraph Authority ensures that the quality of transmission in satisfactory.

Amongst the mentioned transmission systems AF and CF on communications cables is the usual method. *Power-line carrier telephony* is mainly operated via two of the conductor lines on high-tension lines. In principle, however, it is possible to use power-line carrier systems on CF lines such as, for example, on self-supporting aerial cable.

Since the frequencies available for radio links are limited, the use of CF systems, on self-supporting overhead cable, is becoming more and more important. If they are accordingly designed, these can also be used as the lightning protector wire on high-tension lines.

For communications cables laid underground, more and more frequent use is being made of plastic cables with PE (polythene) sheathing, and conductors insulated with solid PE. With paper-insulated cables all the cores usually absorb moisture when the sheath gets damaged, with the result that all the connections carried by the cable are almost simultaneously put out of operation. This, however, is not the case with cables insulated with plastic materials. The higher demands for satisfactory operation ESU installations are thus particularly well satisfied by plastic insulated cables. Before deciding upon the appropriate cable full details must be obtained regarding the possible effects of power and high-voltage installations.

8.4. Telegraphy and data transmission

Telegraphy principally makes use of *digital* transmission processes. In this system the information to be transmitted, which mainly consists of letters and numbers, is converted into a two-bit arrangement (or *binary coding*) and is transmitted serially (digitally).

Digital processes are used in telegraphy, remote control engineering and for data transmission.

For special purposes for instance, in video telegraphy, an analog process is used. In this system the information to be communicated is transmitted, point by point, in the form of separate electrical (analog) quantities corresponding to the shading values they are intended to represent.

The *facsimile process* is a special type of video telegraphy. In this process the information is coded, just as in the digital process, in such a way that a distinction is made only between white and black. The intermediate grey tones are either allotted a white value or a black value. The sphere of application of the facsimile process is thus limited to the transmission of line drawings and manuscripts. The transmission of weather maps is a classic example of its use.

Normal telephone lines can be used for the transmission of video telegraphy and facsimile processes which make no greater demands than normal speech transmission.

8.4.1. Telegraphic transmission engineering

A *telegraphic transmission system* consists, basically of a transmitter, a transmission route (channel) and a receiver. By means of the digital process the message is converted (by keying) into a series of electrical binary signals, which are then transmitted to the receiver via the transmission route. The electrical binary signals are then *decoded* by the receiver, i.e., it analyses the binary states (1 or 0) and converts them into the original message.

With reference to keying, a distinction must be made between the following types, when using digital telegraphic processes.

D.C. Keying processes (DCK or GT)

  Single current keying
  Dual current keying

A.C. Keying processes (ACK or WT)

  Single-tone keying with amplitude modulation (AM).
  Dual-tone keying (DACK) with frequency-shift keying (FSK) between two fixed frequencies, or with frequency modulation (FM/ACK).

At the intersection point between the exchange and the ACK equipment, the nominal current for the dual-current keying process is ± 20 mA. The nominal current required by the teleprinters on the line between the exchange and the subscriber, when operated on the single current process, is 40 mA.

The usual means of transmission in telegraphy are, for d.c. telegraphy single, double or four-wire lines which transmit d.c. but, for a.c. telegraphy it is usual to make use of the AF channels of AF lines, CF two-wire lines (using the separate-frequency process) or CF four-wire lines (using the identical-frequency process), where each audio-frequency channel (frequency band 300 to 3400 Hz) can be loaded with up to 24 a.c. telegraphy channels.

In the public communications network the various telegraph lines are distinguished by letters: e.g., TG indicates a normal telegram line, TGX, a connection within the telegraphic selector dialling network (Gentex), TX, a connecting line in the telex network.

Telex is the abbreviation for the English expression "telegraph exchange". The telex network is part of the public telegraphic service. The nominal telegraphic transmission speed for telex is 50 Baud (Bd).

A bit, or binary digit, which consists of two signal elements, is the information unit for a *binary decision*. The symbols, for instance, letters or numbers, or other symbols, are represented as a series of "Yes" or "No" values; i.e., they are represented in "bits". In the *5-element start/stop system* used in the telex system, each symbol (according to the No. 2 International Telegraphic Alphabet) consists of a 5-bit code. In addition, each of the symbols, consisting of five bits, is prefixed by a start element and has a stop element as a suffix. The length of the start element is the same as the length of a *signal element*, but the length of the stop element is one and one-half signal elements in length. The symbol length thus consists of the starting element $+5$ information bits and the stop element which equals 7.5 signal elements.

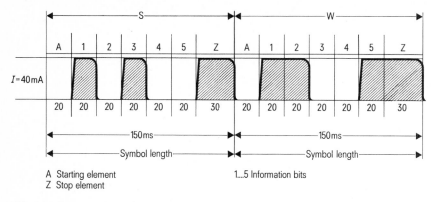

A Starting element   1....5 Information bits
Z Stop element

Fig. 38   Current pattern for letters S and W

Figure 38 shows contemporary patterns of the symbols for the letters S and W.

The length of the standard, shortest, undistorted signal element is denoted by T_0, the unit element. In a 50 digit code the length of a unit is 20 ms.

The telegraphic rate v_s states how many pulses (unit elements) are transmitted per unit of time. The unit for this is the Baud (Bd.). Accordingly, 1 Baud means 1 pulse (unit element) per second.

The telegraphic rate v_s and the length of the unit element T_0 are interrelated.

For example, if the telegraphic rate $v_s = 50$ Bd, then the length of a unit element is

$$T_0 = \frac{1}{v_s} = \frac{1}{50} \text{ s} = 20 \text{ ms}$$

at a telegraphic rate of 200 Bd, the unit element T_0 has a length of 5 ms.

The product of the telegraphic rate, and the number of binary decisions transmitted per element time, is the data transmission rate v_D which is expressed in bit/s. This is the same as the information element rate for the binary code used in telegraphy

$$v_D \text{ } in \text{ } \frac{\text{bit}}{\text{s}} \cong v_s \text{ in Bd} .$$

Another quantity used in telegraph engineering is the *symbol rate* v_z which is known as the signalling output of a telegraph equipment set, or as the teleprinter output of a teleprinter.

$$v_z = \frac{1}{\text{time to transmit each symbol}} .$$

For the example quoted in Fig. 38, the symbol rate is

$$v_z = \frac{1}{150} \cdot 10^{-3} = 6\frac{2}{3} \text{ symbols per second}$$

$$\text{or } 6\frac{2}{3} \cdot 60 = 400 \text{ symbols per minute.}$$

If one or several elements do not have the *nominal period (nominal length)*, then a symbol is considered to be distorted.

The symbol-error frequency is a measure of the quality of the telegraph line. This is the ratio of the number of faulty symbols to the number of symbols transmitted correctly during the transmission. A symbol-error frequency $< 10^{-5}$ is required by, and is generally maintained by, telegraph traffic.

8.4.2. Remote control engineering

As a sign of the increase in automation processes, *remote control techniques* are finding increasing application in the control of production processes and in the transport and distribution of goods such as, for instance, electrical power, crude oil, the initial products of the chemical industries (e.g., pipe-lines for ethylene) and for the control of gas and long-distance water supplies.

Remote control techniques include both *remote control systems* and *remote monitoring* (telemetering) systems. In a remote control system the peripheral equipments are actuated remotely (i.e., switched or adjusted) from the central control station. In a remote monitoring system the flow of information is, basically, in the opposite direction, i.e., the data recorded on the peripheral equipment is indicated in the central station (telemetry and remote display devices).

Where remote control systems have more than two operating points, every message (signal) must have an address (or *station/call sign*). In this way the destination for orders (remote control), and the source of information (remote monitoring), can be unambiguously defined. The call sign (address) is prefixed to the order or message.

After the message to be transmitted has been converted into electrical binary symbols, the simplest way of supplying it to the line is as a series of d.c. pulses by the single-current keying process. *Dual-current keying* is another process for keying d.c. currents. In both systems the lines must transmit d.c. currents i.e., there must be a continuous electrical connection. Since the range of these systems is small, it is usual to convert the d.c. pulses into a form which via suitable transmission lines (e.g., by means of associated modulation processes) facilitates an increase in range.

There exist the following types of transmission lines, and the following methods of transmission:

(a) D.C. transmission lines: two- or four-wire; suitable for the single-current or dual-current keying process (the letter usually only uses four-wire lines); range, up to a loop resistance of some 1.5 kΩ.

(b) A.C. two-wire lines which block d.c. with the associated transformers. The shortest a.c. line is operated at a frequency of 50 Hz. When the transmitter voltage is 60 V a.c., it is possible to tolerate a line attenuation of 21 dB (2.4 Np).

(c) A.C. telegraphy channels (in the audio-frequency range).

(d) Unamplified AF two-wire lines; the AF frequency band may be partially or fully used.

(e) The AF channels of CF two-wire lines (using the two-wire separate-frequency process); the range is similar to the range of the CF system.

(f) Four-wire circuits for the transmission of AF remote-control signals; AF four-wire connections with loaded lines and repeaters are the more generally used. CF four-wire connections (identical-frequency process) are not, however, common in private communications systems.

8.4.3. Long range data transmission

The conventional method of data processing can only supply exact data related to past facts, to circumstances unaffected by time or to circumstances where the period of time involved is predictable. Spheres of activity, where frequently changing actual informations are always required, cannot be automatised and rationalised by this method of data processing, since there is an over-lengthy time interval between the origination of the initial data at the point of origin, and ist arrival, after the results of processing, at the point where it is required.

To provide automatic and efficient transmission of information in the latter sphere of activity, *long range data processing* is used. *Long range data transmission* is thus used, instead of the actual transport of data carriers by persons. The data are thus transmitted via *electrical transmission routes* from their point of origin to a remote processing location, from where the processed results are transmitted to the point where they are required.

With an *indirect (off line) long range data processing* system the transmission time is exclusively confined to data transmission. At the point of origin, the data are recorded on *mechanically-readable data carriers* (e.g., by holes in *punched cards* and in *punched tapes* or by recording the data on *magnetic tape*). These records are usually collected and stored. The *data carriers* are read, at the *data collecting point*, within a data input point connected to the transmission line where the data read are converted into the electrical signals for transmission along the line. At the processing, or computing centre, the *data read-out point* converts the received data signals and reproduces the data on mechanically-readable data carriers. The data read-out point can generally by reached by more than one data input point. The actual method of processing the data is similar to that of the conventional method; it may, therefore, depending on the timetable at the computing centre, require the use of their staff.

In case of *direct (on line) long range data processing* of large quantities of data the transmission path is connected directly to the computer at the place of processing installations. As with off-line data processing the data are recorded and collected at the point of origin; thereafter, however, they are transmitted directly to the data processing centre via the data input point and the transmission line. At the data processing station the incoming information is usually stored temporarily on fast *peripheral stores* such as *magnetic discs*, until it is processed. The processing, which is dependent on the available facilities of the data processing installation is, usually, effected by *multiprogramming*. By this process, although the operator can interfere, the available processing time is automatically distributed by the processing equipment amongst the various tasks requiring to be processed. The processed results, usually, are also stored temporarily on fast peripheral stores in the data-processing installations. The data is fed to the point where it is required, directly from the data-processing installation via the transmission to the output point *(remote batch processing)*. By the temporary storage of the input and processed data on fast peripheral stores, the data-processing equipment can be more economically used. In comparison with the traditional methods of batch processing, remote batch processing thus results in a more economic use of the data-processing equipment, in the relief of the work load on the staff in the computing centre, and, generally, in speedier processing of the data.

The real possibilities of direct long range data processing were, however, only fully exploited by the introduction of *real time processing*. By this system, data from continuously-operated, remotely located, data points are directly entered as questions via transmission routes into a data-processing unit, where they are immediately processed. The processed results are then issued (the answers) immediately to the data point in the location where they are required, which is usually in the same location as the input point. The data points *(dialogue stations)* for this *dialogue* with the data processing unit are, therefore, usually equipped with a key board for the manual input of data, and an apparatus for providing a legible output (e.g., fluorescent screen or printer). The operator at the dialogue station can thus get important information from the data processing unit through its ability to process and answer questions immediately. It is, of course, assumed that the state of information in the data processing unit is continuously amended, where it is liable to alteration or requires to be evaluated before providing an answer. The same assumptions apply to the input data.

Long-range data processing systems which operate on the *dialogue principle* have many spheres of application; for instance, *process control* and *time-sharing operation*. They are also used for booking seats with transport businesses. In such systems the number of available aircraft seats and other relevant data, e.g., for an airline, are centrally stored a computer. All the booking offices for the relevant airline are equipped with dialogue stations which are connected via transmission line to this central processor.

When using "on-line" long-range data processing systems, the central processing unit must have the appropriate equipment *(hardware)* and a properly adapted program *(software)*. In addition to the program which controls the processing and the program to control the input and output systems in the local peripheral equipment, the program must also include means of controlling the transmission of the data and the manner of cooperating with the remote data points.

In addition to the *central unit* which comprises the control unit, arithmetic unit, working storage, a multiplex channel, selector channel and input and output units, the following are also required: *local peripheral input and output units* (e.g., page printers, punch-card readers, punch-card punchers, high-speed printers) and peripheral stores (e.g., magnetic discs, magnetic tape, magnetic-card stores). Moreover, for "on-line" long-range transmission at least one *data transmission unit* is required. This comprises a central part, and parts dependent on the lines, also known as line boosters. Each line booster is connected via the data-transmission unit with one of the transmission lines. In combination with the terminal data equipments this constitutes the data point or data station.

The type of data-transmission equipment used depends on the method of transmission. The terminal data equipments are peripheral equipments (data input and output units, dialogue equipment) located at the remote stations sending out or requiring information.

Usually, the local peripheral equipment is in the same room or, at least, in the same building as the central unit. These equipments are connected to one another (and to the central unit) by *standard interface cable*, which may be only a few metres, or some tens of metres long.

To connect the terminal data equipment to the data transmission unit, the interface cables required are also relatively short. CCITT make a distinction, depending on the transmission rate between the V24 Interface systems (up to 20 kBd) and V37 Interface systems (more than 20 kBd). The interface cables correspondingly differ in their construction. In future, CF or coaxial cables may be also required for the V37 Interface system.

According to the type of transmission system, there are additional d.c. and/or a.c. interfaces e.g., between a.c. keying systems and the line equipment, or (when using broad-band data transmission) between the separate stages in the long-distance equipment (CF transmission).

In addition to the units and concepts, explained in 8.4.1. (Telegraphic transmission engineering) which are, in principle, also used for long-range data transmission techniques, some further concepts are used in data engineering.

In *third-generation* data processing installations (e.g., the Siemens 4004 system) the standard unit of information content is the *"byte"*. One byte contains 8 bits for information and a parity-check bit for error checking.

One byte can either be used to represent a letter of the alphabet, a special symbol, two decimal digits in the *condensed dual code* or a single decimal digit in the *alpha-numeric dual code*.

A data block for transmission is a limited quantity of information which, to ensure correct transmission, can be treated as a unit. Usually, the beginning and end of a block, although the amount of data may vary, is appropriately indicated.

The average amount of information, whether expressed in bits, bytes, halfwords (two consequent bytes), words (four bytes in sequence) fields, sentences, or blocks, which is transmitted in unit time between two consequent equipments in a data transmission system, is known as the transfer rate, v_T, expressed, as a unit, in bits, bytes, words etc. per second, minute, or hour.

In data-transmission processes a distinction must be made between serial and parallel transmission. If all the elements (bits) which belong to one symbol (data signal) are transmitted, one after the other, over the data channel this is described as serial transmission. Under such circumstances the transmission rate and the element rate are the same. On the other hand, when parallel transmission is used, all the bits making up a symbol are transmitted, simultaneously, via several parallel channels. If, in this instance, the data transmission rate is to be the same as that for serial transmission, then n small channels, each having a transmission rate reduced according to $1/n$, will be required. This means, for example, that 1200 bits/s can be transmitted by serial transmission via a single channel at 1200 Baud and by parallel transmission, either via 12 channels at 100 Baud each or via 24 channels at an element rate of 50 Baud. When using parallel transmission it is very often the practice to use only that number of parallel channels as the number of steps (bits) contained in one symbol (data signal) which is to be transmitted. On the assumption that it is only binary pulses which are to be transmitted along the n data channels, then, if the element rate per channel is the same, the amount of data (number of symbols) that can be transmitted in parallel is n times the amount which can be transmitted serially. However, in parallel transmission n times as many bandwidths are required.

The method of operating any long-range data transmission system depends on the operational requirements. Three different methods of operation are possible:

Simplex

(Directional operation). Data can only be transmitted one way; e.g., only from point A to point B.

Semi-duplex

(Alternate operation). Data can be transmitted alternately between points A and B. Such transmissions are only made serially.

Duplex (also termed Full Duplex)

(Dual operation). Data can be simultaneously transmitted from A to B and from B to A.

Telegraphic, telephones, and broad-band methods of transmission can be used for long-range data transmission.

In addition to its primary purpose, which is the exchange of information by telephone, the public-telephone selector dialling system will, also, always be of importance for long-range data transmission. The advantage lies partly in the close multi-looping in this network, partly in its wide ramifications, and partly also in the fact that subscribers can talk to one another on the telephone before and after the transmission of the data.

Data-transmission selector dialling networks, constructed on telegraphic principles like the Telex network, have the advantage that their error rate is lower than in the public telephone network.

The following are the available *telegraphic transmission paths* which have been installed for the transmission of digital signals: the *Telex network*, the *Datex network* and *hired telegraph lines*.

A transmission rate of 50 bit/s is possible on the *Telex network*. The data signals are transmitted to the subscribers connection in the Telex exchange most usually, by single-current keying (120 V d.c., 40 mA), via the two-wire line to the local exchange. At this local telex exchange they are converted into dual-current signals (± 60 V, ± 20 mA) for four-wire lines symmetrical to earth. At such high signal levels, the coding symbols for the exchange are transmitted as well as the data via the selector dialling devices of the telex exchanges. The error rate is, therefore relatively low. For the Telex network, the German Federal Post and Telegraph Authority (DBP) give the probability of error per bit as 5 to $10 \cdot 10^{-6}$. The connection between the Telex exchanges is made via sections of the a.c. telegraph system. In the Telex system the most usual transmission code is The International Telegraphic Alphabet No. 2 with a single start element, and a stop signal of one and a half elements. When using the Telex network for data transmission, remote controlled switch units are required at the data stations whilst, at the data processing centre, a connector unit for data transmission is required for each Telex line connected to it.

In the *Datex network* transmission rates of 200 bit/s are possible. The data signals are most usually transmitted as dual-current signals (± 60 V, ± 20 mA) on a four-wire local line which is symmetrical to earth. Where the subscriber and the Datex exchange are more than 20 km apart use is generally made of a.c. telegraphic transmission equipment. The choice between a transmission code and the common mode method is largely arbitrary. According to DBP the probability of error per bit is 2 to $8 \cdot 10^{-6}$. In the Datex network for data transmission, data remote-controlled switch units are required at the data stations, and one data-transmission connector unit per Datex line is required at the data processing centre. Apart from these differences the operation of the Datex and Telex Systems is the same.

Hired telegraph lines are lines rented for a fee, by the relevant communications company to the user for his sole and continuous use. They can either be switched as fixed two-or four-wire connections or as telegraphic-connections over private exchanges, for example concentrators. The permissible transmission rates are 50, 100 or 200 bit/s. According to DBP the probability of error per bit on hired telegraph lines is 2 to $20 \cdot 10^{-7}$. The choice of a transmission code or the common mode method is arbitrary. Data remote-controlled switch units are required at the data stations, and at the data processing centre, a connector unit is required for each transmission line.

If continuous unloaded transmission lines are available then a *low transmission voltage d.c. data transmission system* (LTDCT) can be operated. With this system transmission rates of up to 10000 bit/s are possible, under special circumstances where the range is limited. The used d.c. data-transmission equipment for low-voltage transmission operates at a transmitter voltage of ± 300 mV. When transmitting at 2400 bit/s it is possible to attain an average probability of error per symbol of 10^{-8} by using dual-current keying, earth-free and earth-symmetrical line, and sub-matching.

Besides interference noise, attenuation distortion and phase distortion, the critical factor in determining range for broad band data transmission with LTDCT systems is the near-end cross-talk on the subscribers cable.

The attenuation unit, $a = \alpha \cdot l$, for the line must be smaller than the cross-talk attenuation unit, a_N, by at least the necessary signal-to-noise ratio r (approximately 32 dB (3.7 Np) for d.c. transmission); otherwise, the received signal will suffer undue interference from the signal being transmitted in the opposite direction.

The permissible length of the conductor in km can be calculated from the equation

$$l = \frac{a_N - r}{\alpha}.$$

The value to be used for the attenuation constant (the attenuation of the line per kilometre) is the value appropriate to the maximum transmission frequency under consideration.

In case of a local subscriber network using paper-insulated or plastic-insulated St III cables (star-twisted, without using a phantom circuit) of, e.g., 0.8 mm diameter, the permissible length of the line, in the present state of telegraphic technology, for a transmission rate of 10 000 bit/s is of the order of 10 km.

This estimate assumes that four-wire duplex operation in separate quads is used for the transmission in both directions. Moreover, the (estimated) noise voltage must be maintained ≤ 0.2 mV.

By virtue of this LTDCT system both duplex and semi-duplex operation are possible using the "start-stop" or synchronous process with any transmission code. If data is transmitted by the synchronous process, a clock-pulse generator is required, either in the d.c. transmission system or in the terminal data equipment, or else the line booster on the side of the data processing equipment must supply the timing pulses.

Equally-high transmission rates, without any limitation on range, can be achieved on *telephone lines* whether they belong (a), to the public telephone system, (b), to a private telephone network, or (c), to a hired telephone line.

It is generally well-known that telephone lines are suitable for the transmission of analogue signals in the audio-frequency band between 300 and 3400 Hz. If digital signals are to be transmitted, however, they must first be converted into analogue signals within this frequency band. Conversely, the analogue signals at the receiver must be reconverted into digital signals for further use. The data-transmission devices which perform these functions are called *modems* (Modulator-demodulator). They are used at the data station and also at the data processing installation.

The modems used in the *public telephone network* for the serial transmission of symbols and bits with respectively 200 bit/s and 600/1200 bit/s use binary frequency-modulation.

The series modems for 200 bit/s also make duplex operation possible on two-wire continuous subscriber lines in the public telephone system, i.e., data can be simultaneously transmitted in both directions at 200 bit/s. For this purpose the audio-frequency band is divided into two transmission channels. Channel A is at a frequency of 1080 ± 100 Hz, and channel B at a frequency of 1750 ± 100 Hz.

With series modems for 600/1200 bit/s it is only possible to use semi-duplex operation on two-wire telephone lines; i.e., data can be alternately sent and received. Duplex operation is possible on four-wire lines. For transmission over lines which do not have CCITT approval, the modem can be switched over to 600 bit/s. In such instances the frequency used is 1500 ± 200 Hz. When transmitting at 1200 bit/s a frequency of 1700 ± 400 Hz is used.

According to data published by the DBP the error probability per bit on the public selector-dialling telephone network is 2 to $10 \cdot 10^{-6}$ at a rate of 200 bit/s, and 1 to $10 \cdot 10^{-5}$ at rates of 600/1200 bit/s.

The same modems as are used on the public telephone system are used for data transmission on *private telephone networks*. Because of the value of the error probability per bit, it is sometimes worth considering whether it may not be possible to work at a higher transmission rate than is possible on the public selector dialling network.

Data can be transmitted bit-serially at rates up to 4800 bit/s on *hired telephone lines*. With the exception of the error probability per bit, which is about 1 to $10 \cdot 10^{-6}$, and the possibility of duplex operation at 1200 bit/s via four-wire lines, the information given regarding data-transmission via the public telephone system is equally true on these hired systems for transmission rates up to 1200 bit/s.

Rates of data transmission between 1200 bit/s and 4800 bit/s can be achieved with series modems which operate synchronously, but the required timing must either be produced in the modem or must be supplied by the terminal data equipment.

For transmission rates greater than 4800 bit/s the communications authorities have made *wideband transmission routes* available. These have been derived from the basic primary groups (in the frequency band 60 to 108 kHz) or from the basic supergroups (in the frequency band 312 to 552 kHz) in normal CF systems. With these routes transmission rates of 40 and 200 kbit/s are possible.

Where companies or administrative offices have their own internal data lines, whether for a large computer installation, or for a so-called on-line computer, it is also common to use d.c. process for data transmission. CF connections are rare in this sphere, since the cost of equipment, when taking into consideration the short transmission route, is relatively high. On the other hand, AF connections are worthwhile even although repeaters and compensators may have to be paid for.

As regards any possible mutual interference (noise) between the two transmission lines, there are no problems with communications cables solely used for data transmission. However, if other communications systems which are in operation along the same cable, have peaks of noise (acoustic shock), these could interfere with the data transmission.

When operating clock installations, Ela-installations, inductive selector systems, sometimes, even remote-control devices and such like, very high interference-pulses may occur in the cable. In such instances, preference should be given to the use of a separate cable run.

Falsification of the bit information (error probability per bit) is mainly due to interference in the technical equipment used to transmit the data, e.g., the data-transmission device, or to interference in the transmission route caused, particularly by other technical equipment. Various protective measures are used to detect and, where possible, correct errors in the transmission of data, but these methods cannot detect any error made during the recording and/or processing of the data.

Because the probabilities of errors due to disturbances in the transmission routes are greater, by several orders of magnitude, than those due to interference within the data transmitting equipment, the characteristics of the data transmission line must be carefully considered to ensure the accuracy of the data. As regards the average error probabilities per bit already given, it should be noted that these probabilities of error are not constant. Periods of high error-probability (group disturbances) alternate with periods of low error-probability, or periods of random error distribution (stochastic disturbances).

If a long-range data-processing system is to operate efficiently then, in addition to the correct choice of the equipment (programmed and other technical apparatus), and the choice of a suitable transmission code, the proper choice of a suitable transmission procedure is of particular importance. This involves determination of the data-transmission process and also the measures to be adopted when errors in transmission occur. The design of the data-transmission "blocks" (type, number and arrangement of the data transmission control signals, and the actual information signals), the method of synchronisation (start-stop, or synchronous method) and the method of operation (directional, semi-duplex or duplex operation) and the checking process (by symbols or by "blocks") etc. are all dependent on the selected data transmission procedure.

Type codes for communications cables and wires

The VDE (Association of German Electrical Engineers) has laid down uniform codes for the make-up elements of cables and wires. These codes are generally applied by the German cable industry and the users of cables (e.g. The German Federal Post Office and the German Federal Railways).

The standard type codes used in the field of communications cable engineering characterize the essential elements of the cable make-up, such as conductor insulation, shielding, sheath, serving, number of conductors and conductor diameter. The make-up is designated from the center to the outer layers beginning with the conductor insulation, by means of various codes each of which has its own exactly defined meaning, e. g. "A-PMbc = outdoor cable with paper insulation, lead sheath, armoring and serving".

For new cable types not yet contained in the VDE Regulations or in order to specify additional features the cable firms use their own codes in the form of letters or figures.

Type codes arranged in alphabetical and numerical order

Letters (alphabetical)

A–	outdoor cable
AB–	outdoor cable with lightning protection
AD–	outdoor cable for power line protection (e.g. differential protection)
AJ–	outdoor cable with protection against inductive influences
(...Al)	... total cross-section of aluminium shield in mm^2
b	armoring
B	baked coils
B	whipping made of textile fibers
(1 B ...)	one layer of steel tape; ... thickness of the steel tape in mm
(2 B ...)	two layers of steel tape; ... thickness of a steel tape in mm
Bd	unit-type stranding
bl	blue
blk	bare conductor, not insulated
br	brown
Bz II	bronze conductor
c	serving of jute and compound

C	outer conductor or shield of copper wire braiding
(C)	shield of copper wire braiding over one single stranding element
c–K	reinforced serving of paper tape, jute and compound
Cu	copper conductor
(... Cu)	... total cross-section of copper shield in mm^2
D	outer conductor or shield of copper wire whipping
(D)	shield of copper wire whipping over one single stranding element
Da	shield of aluminium wire whipping
DM	multiple twin
e	additional copper conductor
E	protective cover with embedded layer of plastic tape
el	ivory color
f	fine wire design
F	foil insulation
F	flat constructional design for installation wires
F	continuous blocking
F	star quad with utilization of the phantom circuit, used for railway communication cables according VDE
(F ...)	flat wire; ... thickness of the wire in mm
(fA)	longitudinally applied aluminium tape, only in conjunction with (St)
Fe	steel wire
(F..Gbvzk..)	flat wire, galvanized; ... thickness of the wire in mm, with steel tape counter helix; ... tensile strength in daN/mm^2
(fK)	longitudinally applied copper tape, only in conjunction with (St)
FL–	flat line with solid conductor(s)
FLi–	flat line with stranded conductor(s)
G	insulation of natural rubber or styrenebutadiene rubber
2G	silicon rubber insulation (SJR)
3G	isobuthylene isoprene rubber insulation (JJR) or ethylene propylene rubber (EPR)
4G	ethylenevinylacetate insulation (EVA)
5G	chloroprene rubber insulation (CR)
6G	chlorosulfonated polyethylene insulation (CSM)
7G	fluorelastics insulation
8G	nitrilic rubber insulation (NBR)
G–	mine cable
ge	yellow
GJ–	mine cable with protection against inductive influences
gn	green
gr	gray
Gs	glass fiber whipping or braiding
2Gs	2 layers of glass fiber whipping or braiding

h	increased heat resistance
H	natural rubber (NR) or styrenebutadiene jacket
2H	jacket of silicon rubber
3H	jacket of isobuthylene isoprene rubber or ethylene propylene rubber (EPR)
4H	jacket of ethylenevinylacetate
5H	jacket of chloroprene rubber
6H	jacket of chlorosulfonated polyethylene
7H	jacket of fluorelastics
8H	jacket of nitrilic rubber
(H ...)	maximum values of mutual capacitance in nF/km
(hS)	semi-conductive tape or layer
J	value of insulation resistance guaranteed (for enamelled wires)
–J	international protective wire
J–	installation cable
(JfA)	inner jacket plus longitudinally applied aluminium tape, only in conjunction with (St)
... iMF	individual stranding elements (e.g. pairs = PiMF or conductors = AiMF) in metallic foil or in metallized paper and additional wire
iMF	several stranding elements (e.g. stranded layers) in metallic foil or in metallized paper and additional wire
K	smooth copper tape applied longitudinally, welded
(K)	inner jacket plus longitudinally folded copper tape
kf ...	cold-proof design up to minus ...°C
Kh	hard-drawn copper conductor
L	enamel coat of conductor or varnish on insulation
L	smooth aluminium sheath
L–	insulated line
(L)	shield of plastic-covered aluminium tape
(L)2Y	laminated sheath
2L	double enamel coat as insulation
(LA)	enamelled conductor
LD	corrugated aluminium sheath or outer conductor
Lg	stranding in layers
Li	stranded or twisted conductor (litz wire)
lld	airtight longitudinally (in the case of wires for loading coil boxes and separating plugs)
(LP)	enamelled pair
(LV)	enamelled quad
M	lead sheath
M	special cable
(M ...)	max. mean value of mutual capacitance in nF/km

(mS)	magnetic shield
Mz	alloyed lead sheath
N	for normal conditions (for enamelled wires)
nf	natural-colored
O	without plastic tape between conductors and shield (only in the case of connecting wires)
ö	oil-proof
or	orange
P	paper insulation
P	pair twisting
perf	perforated
Ps	polyethylene disks for coaxial pairs
Pw	polyethylene helix for coaxial pairs
r	grooved (e.g. metal tube outer conductor)
(r .../...)	max. permissible reflection factor in ... % at ... MHz
(R ...)	round wire; ... diameter of the wire in mm
RCu	beaded copper tape as outer conductor
RFe	beaded steel tape
(R..Gbvzk..)	round wire, galvanized; ... thickness of the wire in mm, with steel tape counter helix; ... tensile strength in daN/mm^2
(... RP)	... number of reserve pairs
rs	pink
rt	red
S	silk whipping
S	railway signal cable
(S ...)	nominal value of mutual capacitance in nF/km
S–	switchboard cable
Si	cables for industrial electronics (e.g. SIMATIC®)
2S	2 layers of silk whipping
St	star quad with utilization of phantom circuit according VDE
(St)	static shield of metal tape or plastic-backed metal foil
St I	star quad in long-distance cables according VDE
St III	star quad in local cables according VDE
Staku	copper clad steel wire
steg	flat twin wire with web
sw	black
T	supporting element of steel, textile or plastic
TF	carrier frequency cable or carrier frequency quad
Tk	copper outer conductor (tube-shaped)
(TR ...)	supporting element of round wire; ... diameter of the wire in mm
trop	tropicalized protective compound in the protective covers
U	braiding of textile fibers

V	directly solderable (for enamelled wires)
V	tinned copper conductor
vi	violet
vs	silver plated
vzk	galvanized
vzn	tinned
W	higher temperature resistance (for enamelled wires)
W	corrugated steel sheath
Wk	sheath, shield or outer conductor of welded, corrugated copper tape
ws	white
X	cover made of interlaced polyvinylchloride
2X	cover made of interlaced polyethylene
10X	cover made of interlaced polyvinylidenefluorid
Y	insulation, protective cover or sheath of polyvinylchloride (PVC)
Yv	reinforced protective cover of polyvinylchloride (PVC)
2Y	insulation, sheath or cover of polyethylene (PE)
02Y	cellular polyethylene insulation
2Yho	polyethylene air-spaced insulation
2Yn	low-pressure polyethylene insulation
2Yv	reinforced polyethylene protective cover (PE)
3Y	polystyrene insulation
4Y	polyamide cover or sheath
5Y	polytetrafluorethylene insulation or cover (PTFE)
6Y	fluor-ethylene-propylene cover
7Y	ethylene-tetra-fluorethylene cover
8Y	polyimide cover
9Y	polypropylene cover
10Y	polyvinylidenefluorid cover
11Y	polyurethane cover
12Y	polyterephthalic esters cover
–Z	with printed numbers
Z	twin wire
(Z)	tensile-proof braiding of steel or polyamide wires
(Z …/…)	max. permissible deviation of characteristic impedance in … % at … MHz

Numbers

The number of conductors or pairs and the conductor dimensions are designated by figures interconnected by the symbol "x":
Number of conductors x 1 x diameter or cross-section in the case of single conductor stranding.

Number of pairs x 2 x diameter or cross-section in the case of pair or quad twisting.
Number of conductors x 3 x diameter or cross-section in the case of triple twisting.
Number of conductors x 4 x diameter or cross-section in the case of quad twisting.

In the case of wires and strands twisted in open formation (connecting wires and connecting strands) only the number of conductors x conductor dimensions are indicated.

In the case of switchboard cables produced with pair, triple, quad or quintuple twisting, the number of twisted elements x twisting type is indicated. For example, a 50-wire switchboard cable with twisting in quintuple formation and with a conductor diameter of 0.6 mm is designated S–Y (St) Y 10 x 5 x 0.6.

In the case of switchboard cables with conductors stranded singly not only the number of conductors is indicated, but also the number of color groups and the number of different wire colors in parentheses. For example, a 60-wire switchboard cable with 6 color groups and 10 different wire colors is designated as S–YY 60 (6 x 10) x 1 x 0.5.

The diameter of solid conductors is indicated in mm, the cross-section of stranded conductors in mm^2.

In the case of coaxial elements the outer diameter of the inner conductor and the inner diameter of the outer conductor (i.e. the diameter above the insulation) are stated in mm, e.g. 2.6/9.5.

In the VDE Regulations the electrical characteristics, particularly the mutual capacitance, are indicated by letters and Roman numerals, e.g. St I, St III.

In the cable industry any deviation from the mutual capacitance values of the VDE Regulations is indicated in parentheses as a mean value in nF/km, e.g. (S50).

The maximum mutual capacitance values demanded are indicated by (H ...), e.g. (H55). The mutual capacitance value is also stated for carrier frequency cables, e.g. TF (H 28).

Examples

Local cable A-PMbc 30 x 2 x 0.8 St III (F 0.8)

A–	outdoor cable
P	paper insulation
M	lead sheath
b	armoring
c	serving of jute and compound
30 x 2	30 pairs
0.8	conductor diameter in mm
St III	star quad in local cables according to VDE
(F 0.8)	flat wire, thickness of wire 0.8 mm

Signal cable A-2YYbY 56 x 1 x 1.4 S (1B 0.3)

A–	outdoor cable
2Y	polyethylene insulation (PE)
Y	polyvinylchloride sheath (PVC)
b	armoring
Y	polyvinylchloride serving (PVC)
56 x 1	56 conductors
1.4	conductor diameter in mm
S	railway signal cable
(1B0.3)	1 layer of steel tape, 0.3 mm thick

RF cable   2YCY 1.0/4.5–60 Li

2Y	polyethylene (PE) insulation
C	shield of copper wire braiding
Y	polyvinylchloride (PVC) sheath
1.0	diameter of inner conductor in mm
4.5	diameter above the insulation in mm
60	characteristic impedance 60 Ω
Li	stranded conductor

Coaxial carrier long-distance cable A- $\dfrac{\text{PsTk}}{\dfrac{\text{P}}{\text{P}}}$ LEbEc $\dfrac{6 \times 2.6/9.5}{\dfrac{14 \times 2 \times 0.9\,\text{TF (H33)}}{12 \times 2 \times 0.9\,\text{St I}}}$ (2B 0.5)

A–	outdoor cable
Ps	polyethylene disks
Tk	outer conductor of copper (tube-shaped)
P	paper insulation
L	aluminium sheath
E	protective cover with embedded layer of plastic tape
b	armoring
c	serving of jute and compound
6	number of coaxial pairs
2.6/9.5	diameter of inner conductor/inner diameter of outer conductor in mm
14 x 2	14 pairs
12 x 2	12 pairs
0.9	conductor diameter in mm
TF (H33)	carrier frequency quad, maximum mutual capacitance value of a side-circuit 33 nF/km
St I	star quad in long-distance cables according to VDE
(2B 0.5)	two layers of steel tape, each layer having a thickness of 0.5 mm

Type codes arranged according to make-up criteria

Code for designating the application purposes

A–	outdoor cable
AB–	outdoor cable with lightning protection
AD–	outdoor cable for power line protection (e.g. differential protection)
AJ–	outdoor cable with protection against inductive influences
FL–	flat line with solid conductor(s)
FLi–	flat line with stranded conductor(s)
G–	mine cable
GJ–	mine cable with protection against inductive influences
J–	installation cable
L–	insulated line
M	special cable
S–	switchboard cable
S	railway signal cable
Si	cables for industrial electronics (e.g. SIMATIC®)

Code for designating the make-up elements

Designation of the wire insulation

B	suitable for baked coils (for enamelled wires)
B	whipping made of textile fibers
F	foil insulation
G	insulation of natural rubber or styrenebutadiene rubber
2G	silicon rubber insulation (SJR)
3G	isobuthylene isoprene rubber insulation (JJR) or ethylene/propylene rubber (EPR)
4G	ethylenevinylacetate insulation (EVA)
5G	chloroprene rubber insulation (CR)
6G	chlorosulfonated polyethylene insulation (CSM)
7G	fluorelastics insulation
8G	nitrilic rubber insulation (NBR)
Gs	glass fiber whipping or braiding
2Gs	2 layers of glass fiber whipping or braiding
J	value of insulation resistance guaranteed (for enamelled wires)
–J	international protective wire
L	enamel coat of conductor or varnish on insulation
(LA)	enamelled conductor
(LP)	enamelled pair
(LV)	enamelled quad

® Registered Trade Mark

2L	double enamel coat as insulation
N	for normal conditions (for enamelled wires)
P	paper insulation
Ps	polyethylene disks for coaxial pairs
Pw	polyethylene helix for coaxial pairs
S	silk whipping
2S	2 layers of silk whipping
U	braiding of textile fibers
V	directly solderable (for enamelled wires) higher temperature resistance (for enamelled wires)
X	insulation made of interlaced polyvinylchloride
2X	insulation made of interlaced polyethylene
10X	insulation made of interlaced polyvinylidenefluorid
Y	polyvinylchloride (PVC) insulation
2Y	polyethylene (PE) insulation
2Yho	polyethylene air-spaced insulation
2Yn	low-pressure polyethylene insulation
02Y	cellular polyethylene insulation
3Y	polystyrene insulation
4Y	polyamide insulation
5Y	polytetrafluorethylene insulation (TFE)
6Y	fluor-ethylene-Propylene insulation
7Y	ethylene-tetra-fluorethylene insulation
8Y	polyimide insulation
9Y	polypropylene insulation
10Y	polyvinylidenefluorid insulation
12Y	polyterephthalic esters insulation
–Z	with printed numbers

Designation of the conductor

blk	bare conductor, not insulated
Bz II	bronze conductor
Cu	copper conductor
(... Cu)	... total cross-section of copper shield in mm^2
f	fine wire design
Fe	steel wire
Kh	hard-drawn copper conductor
Li	stranded or twisted conductor (litz wire)
Staku	copper clad steel wire
Tk	copper outer conductor (tube-shaped)
V	tinned copper conductor

vs	silver plated
vzk	galvanized
vzn	tinned

Designation of sheaths, shields and braids

(... Al)	... total cross-section of aluminium shield in mm^2
C	shield of copper wire braiding
(C)	shield of copper wire braiding over one single stranding element
(... Cu)	... total cross-section of copper shield in mm^2
D	shield of copper wire whipping
(D)	shield of copper wire whipping over one single stranding element
Da	shield of aluminium wire whipping
e	additional copper conductor
(fA)	longitudinally applied aluminium tape, only in conjunction with (St)
(fK)	longitudinally applied copper tape, only in conjunction with (St)
H	natural rubber (NR) or styrenebutadiene jacket
2H	jacket of silicon rubber
3H	jacket of isobuthylene isoprene rubber or ethylene propylene rubber (EPR)
4H	jacket of ethylenevinylacetate
5H	jacket of chloroprene rubber
6H	jacket of chlorosulfonated polyethylene
7H	jacket of fluorelastics
8H	jacket of nitrilic rubber
(hS)	semi-conductive tape or layer
(JfA)	inner jacket plus longitudinally applied aluminium tape, only in conjunction with (St)
... iMF	individual stranding elements (e.g. pairs = PiMF or conductors = AiMF) in metallic foil or in metallized paper and additional wire
iMF	several stranding elements (e.g. stranded layers) in metallic foil or in metallized paper and additional wire
K	smooth copper tape applied longitudinally, welded
(K)	inner jacket plus longitudinally applied copper tape
L	smooth aluminium sheath
(L)	shield of plastic-covered aluminium tape
(L)2Y	laminated sheath
LD	corrugated aluminium sheath or outer conductor
M	lead sheath
(mS)	magnetic shield
Mz	alloyed lead sheath
r	grooved (e.g. metal tube outer conductor)

RCu	beaded copper tape as outer conductor
RFe	beaded steel tape
(St)	static shield of metal tape or plastic-backed metal foil
W	corrugated steel sheath
Wk	sheath, shield or outer conductor of welded, corrugated copper tape
X	sheath made of interlaced polyvinylchloride
2X	sheath made of interlaced polyethylene
10X	sheath made of interlaced polyvinylidenefluorid
Y	polyvinylchloride (PVC) sheath
2Y	polyethylene (PE) sheath
4H	polyamide sheath
5Y	polytetrafluorethylene
6Y	fluor-ethylene-Propylene sheat
7Y	ethylene-tetra-fluorethylene sheath
8Y	polyimide sheath
9Y	polypropylene sheath
10Y	polyvinylidenfluorid sheath
11Y	polyurethane sheath

Designation of armoring and protective covers

b	armoring
(1B ...)	one layer of steel tape; ... thickness of the steel tape in mm
(2B ...)	two layers of steel tape; ... thickness of the steel tape in mm
c	serving of jute and compound
c-K	reinforced serving of paper tape, jute and compound
E	protective cover with embedded layer of plastic tape
(F ...)	flat wire; ... thickness of the wire in mm
(F..Gbvzk..)	flat wire, galvanized; ... thickness of the wire in mm, with steel tape counter helix; ... tensile strength in daN/mm^2
kf ...	cold-proof design up to minus ...°C
ö	oil-proof
(R ...)	round wire; ... thickness of the wire in mm
(R..Gbvzk..)	round wire, galvanized; ... thickness of the wire in mm, with steel tape counter helix; ... tensile strength in daN/mm^2
T	supporting element of steel, textile or plastic
(TR ...)	supporting element of round wire; ... diameter of the wire in mm
trop	tropicalized protective compound in the protective covers
U	braiding of textile fibers
X	protective cover made of interlaced polyvinylchloride
2X	protective cover made of interlaced polyethylene

Y	protective cover of polyvinylchloride (PVC)
Yv	reinforced protective cover of polyvinylchloride (PVC)
2Y	protective cover of polyethylene (PE)
2Yv	reinforced protective cover of polyethylene (PE)
(Z)	tensile-proof braiding of steel or polyamide wires

Code for designating the mutual capacitance and type of twisting

Bd	unit-type stranding
DM	multiple twin
F	star quad with utilization of phantom circuit, used for railway communication cables according to VDE
F	flat constructional design for installation wires
(H ...)	maximum value of mutual capacitance in nF/km
(M ...)	max. mean value of mutual capacitance in nF/km
Lg	stranding in layers
P	pair twisting
(r.../...)	max. permissible reflection factor in ... % at ... MHz
(... RP)	... number of reserve pairs
(S ...)	nominal value of mutual capacitance in nF/km
St	star quad with utilization of phantom circuit according to VDE
St I	star quad in long-distance cables according to VDE
St III	star quad in local cables according to VDE
steg	flat twin wire with web
TF	carrier frequency cable or carrier frequency quad
Z	twin wire
(Z .../...)	max. permissible deviation of characteristic impedance in ... % at ... MHz

Special codes

F	continuous blocking
h	increased heat resistance
lld	airtight longitudinally (in the case of wires for loading coil boxes and separating plugs)
O	without plastic tape between conductors and shield (only in the case of connecting wires)
perf	perforated

Color of the insulation and/or of the sheath

bl	blue	or	orange
br	brown	rs	pink
el	ivory	rt	red
ge	yellow	sw	black
gn	green	vi	violet
gr	gray	ws	white
nf	natural-colored		

Compilation of abbreviations used

AC	alternate current
ACK	a.c. keying process ($\hat{=}$ WT)
AF	audio frequency ($\hat{=}$ VF)
AM	amplitude modulation
AtFk	trunk distributing cable
CCITT	International Telegraph and Telephone Consultative Committee
CF	carrier frequency
PLC	CF transmission via power lines
DACK	dual tone keying
DB	German Federal Railways
DBP	German Federal Post and Telegraphy Autority
DC	direct current
DCK	d.c. keying process ($\hat{=}$ GT)
DIN	German Industrial Standard
DM	Dieselhorst-Martin
E	receiver
EMF	electromotive force
ESU	electric power-supply company
Fk	trunk cables in the older network, old broad band cables, coil-loaded CF-cables with short loading sections
FSK	frequency-shift keying
G	four-wire termination
HF	high frequency
JI	junction installation
KxFk	long-distance coaxial cable
LT	d.c. telegraphy
LTDCT	low transmission voltage d.c. data transmission system
LTE	local telephone exchange ($\hat{=}$ OVst)
N	balancing network
NLT	negative line resistance with transistors
NOSFER	New Master System for the determination of reference equivalents
OFk	local trunk cable
OVst	local exchange ($\hat{=}$ LTE)
PE	polyethylene
PED	PE dispersion
PiMF	pair in metal foil
PVC	polyvinylchloride
RC	receiving centre
RMS	effective value (volts)
RRE	receiving reference equivalent
S	transmitter

SRE	sending reference equivalent	TV	television
SUB	subscriber	V	four-wire
TFFk	long-distance CF cable	VDE	German Association of
TFVk	CF connection cable		Electrical Engineers
TG	normal telegram line	VF	voice frequency ($\widehat{=}$ AF)
TGX	connection within the	W	directional switch
	telegraphic selector dialling	WT	a.c. telegraphy
	network	Z	two-wire
TI	terminal installation		
TX	connecting line in the Telex		
	network		

Compilation of the most important symbols used in the formulae

Latin letters

a	attenuation unit	in dB(Np)
a_B	operative attenuation unit	in dB(Np)
a_F	return loss unit	in dB(Np)
a_f	far-end cross-talk attenuation unit	in dB(Np)
a_G	signal-to-noise ratio	in dB(Np)
a_K	harmonic distortion unit	in dB(Np)
a_N	cross-talk attenuation unit	in dB(Np)
a_n	near-end cross-talk attenuation unit	in dB(Np)
a_R	over-all attenuation unit	in dB(Np)
b	phase (angle) unit	in rad
C_B	mutual capacitance (capacity)	in $\dfrac{nF}{km}$
c_{Sp}	coil capacitance per loading section	in nF
D	diameter beneath the sheath	in mm
d	conductor diameter	in mm
f	frequency	in Hz
f_0	cut-off frequency	in Hz
F_{max}	maximum permissible tensile force	in daN
G	net weight of cable	in $\dfrac{daN}{km}$
g	propagation unit	
I_K	short-circuit current	in kA
I_N	nominal current	in kA

k	capacitive coupling (unbalance)	in pF
k	distortion factor	
L	inductance	in $\dfrac{mH}{km}$
l	length of the line	in km
l_{max}	maximum permissible drawing length	in m
L_{Sp}	coil inductance per loading section	in mH
M	mutual inductance between the line causing the interference and the line subjected to the interference	in $\dfrac{mH}{km}$
m	magnetic coupling	in nH
P	power	in W
P_G	noise output	pW
p	level	in dB(Np)
p_m	absolute power level	in dB(Np)
p_r	relative level	in dB(Np)
p_s	absolute voltage level	in dB(Np)
Q	cross-section of the metal sheath	in mm^2
q	cross-section of the conductor	in mm^2
R	conductor resistance, loop resistance	in $\dfrac{\Omega}{km}$
R_e	earthing resistance	in Ω
R_{is}	insulation resistance	in M$\Omega \cdot$ km
R_k	coupling resistance	in Ω
r	reflexion factor	
r_u	reduction factor of the communications cable	
s	length of loading section	in km
t	temperature	in °C
U_G	noise voltage	in mV
U_N	useful voltage	in V
v_p	phase velocity	in $\dfrac{km}{s}$
v_s	telegraphic rate (path velocity)	in Bd
$v_{\ddot{u}}$	transmission velocity	in $\dfrac{bit}{s}$
v_z	symbol rate	in $\dfrac{symbols}{s}$
W	resistance of the balance network	in Ω
X_i	inductive resistance	in $\dfrac{\Omega}{km}$
X_l	inductive resistance of conductor and earth	in $\dfrac{\Omega}{km}$

Z_i	characteristic impedance (imaginary part)	in Ω
Z_L	(complex) characteristic impedance	in Ω
Z_r	characteristic impedance (real part)	in Ω

Greek letters

α	attenuation constant	in $\dfrac{dB}{km}\left(\dfrac{Np}{km}\right)$
α	temperature coefficient	
α_G	leakage attenuation constant	in $\dfrac{dB}{km}\left(\dfrac{Np}{km}\right)$
α_R	resistance attenuation constant	in $\dfrac{dB}{km}\left(\dfrac{Np}{km}\right)$
β	phase constant (wavelength constant)	in $\dfrac{rad}{km}$
γ	propagation constant	in $\dfrac{1}{km}$
$\tan\delta$	dissipation (leakage-current loss) factor	
ε	resulting dielectric constant	
ε_r	relative dielectric constant	
$\tan\varepsilon$	resistance loss factor	
ϑ	depth of penetration	in mm
$\varkappa$	electrical conductivity	in $\dfrac{S\cdot m}{mm^2}$
λ	wavelength	in m
ϱ	specific resistance	in $\dfrac{\Omega\cdot mm^2}{m}$
$\sigma_{max\,zul}$	maximum permissible tensile stress	in $\dfrac{daN}{mm^2}$
τ_g	group propagation time	in $\dfrac{s}{km}$
τ_p	phase delay time	in $\dfrac{s}{km}$
Φ	magnetic flow	in Wb

210

Index

German terms

217

German terms

222

223

German terms

German terms

Digitale Übertragung
Telegrafie-Übertragung
Übertragungstechnik
Übertragungs-Gleichungen
Übertragungsfaktor
Datenfernübertragungsleitung
Bildtelegrafie-Übertragungsleitung
Übertragungsweg
Telegrafie-Übertragungsweg
Leitungstheorie
Übertragungsqualität
Übertragungsstrecke
Elektrische Übertragungsstrecke
Breitband-Übertragungsstrecke
Übertragungssystem
Sprachfrequenz-Übertragungssystem
Trägerfrequenz-Übertragungssystem
Gleichstromdatenübertragung mit
   niedriger Sendespannung

Datenübertragungseinheit
Effektiv übertragenes Frequenzband
Sender
Amtsverbindungskabel
Fernvermittlung
Fernvermittlungstechnik
Fernleitungsübertrager
Weitverkehrsnetz
Fernwahlübertragung
Tube, Rohr
Hohlader
Drallänge
Zweidraht-Frequenzgleichlage-
   Verfahren
Zweidraht-Frequenzgetrenntlage-
   Verfahren
Zweidraht-Dienstleitung
Nachrichtenkabeltypen

Erdkopplung
Unverständliches (nicht lineares)
   Nebensprechen

Bündel
Hauptbündel
Bündelverseilung
Dämpfungsmaß
Nebensprechdämpfungsmaß
Betriebsdämpfungsmaß
Übertragungsmaß
Phasen (-Winkel-)maß